Master the Maths basics with CGP!

This Foundation Question Book from CGP is perfect for helping pupils get to grips with Maths in Year 6.

It's packed with test-style practice on the most important Maths skills, carefully written to build their confidence.

We've also included mixed-topic tests for the start and end of the year, plus answers to every question at the back of the book!

What CGP is all about

Our sole aim here at CGP is to produce the highest quality books — carefully written, immaculately presented and dangerously close to being funny.

Then we work our socks off to get them out to you — at the cheapest possible prices.

Contents

Section Five — Algebra

Section Six — Measurement

Section Seven — Geometry

Section Eight — Statistics

Published by CGP

Editors:
Liam Dyer, Shaun Harrogate, Tom Miles, Rosa Roberts, Ruth Wilbourne.

ISBN: 978 1 78908 046 9

With thanks to Alison Griffin and Dave Ryan for the proofreading.
Also thanks to Jan Greenway for the copyright research.

Printed by Elanders Ltd, Newcastle upon Tyne.
Clipart from Corel®

Based on the classic CGP style created by Richard Parsons.

About This Book

This Book is Full of Year 6 Maths Questions

You'll learn a lot of new maths in Year 6.
This foundation book has questions on all the maths for Year 6 at a slightly easier level — so it's perfect if you're getting to grips with the Year 6 topics.
It matches our Year 6 Study Book. This can help you if you get stuck.

This book covers the Attainment Targets for Year 6 of the 2014 National Curriculum.

The questions in Sections 1-8 are all colour-coded to show how difficult they are.

Easy

2
Harder

Challenge

The answers to all of the questions are at the back of this book.

This book also has two Objectives Tests.
The one at the front of the book is to test that you remember the maths you learnt in Year 5. The test at the back of the book is to see how well you know the maths in this book.

There are Learning Objectives on All Pages

Learning objectives say what you should be able to do.
Use the tick circles to show how confident you feel.

You can use the tick boxes for ongoing assessment to record which attainment targets have been met. Printable checklists of all the objectives can be found at www.cgpbooks.co.uk/primarymaths.

Tick this circle if you can do all the maths on the page.

Tick here if you think you need a bit more practice.

If you're really struggling, tick here.

"I can multiply a four-digit number by a two-digit number."

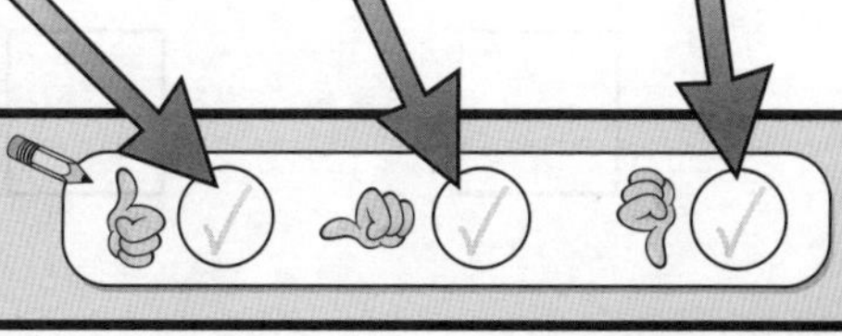

Year Five Objectives Test

1 What is 4.5 × 100?

Circle the correct answer.

0.45 45 450 45 000

1 mark

2 The grid below is made of 100 equal squares.

What percentage of the grid is shaded?

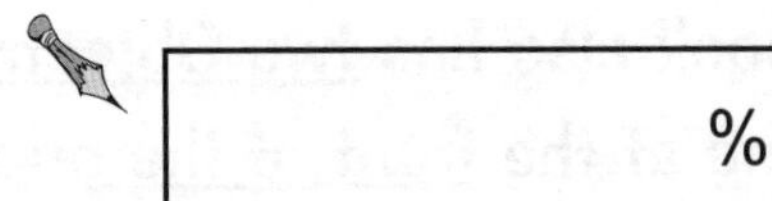

1 mark

3 Work out the calculations below.

Use the number line to help you.

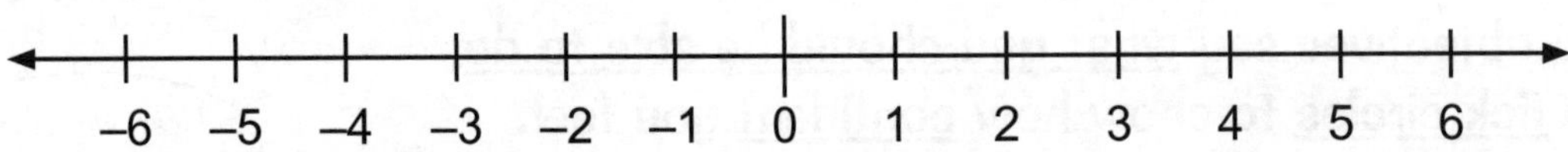

–2 + 6

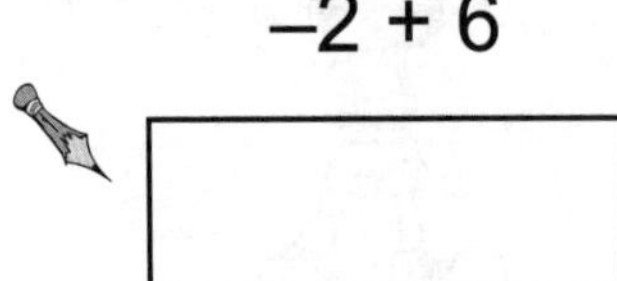

5 – 8

2 marks

4 Tick the Roman numeral which represents 150.

ML CL DL XL

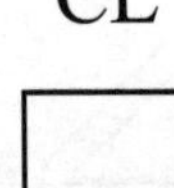

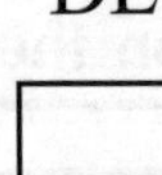

1 mark

5 Fill in the missing numbers.

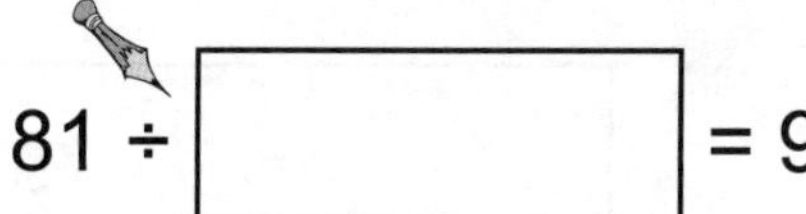

81 ÷ ☐ = 9   810 ÷ ☐ = 9

1 mark

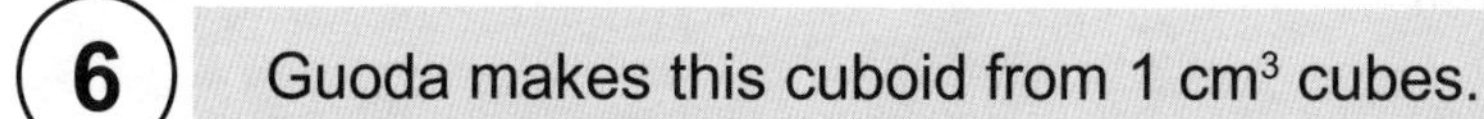

6 Guoda makes this cuboid from 1 cm^3 cubes.

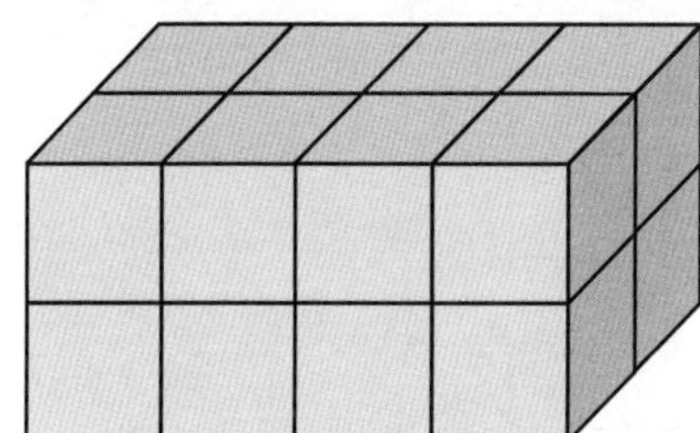

What is the volume of her cuboid?

☐ cm^3

1 mark

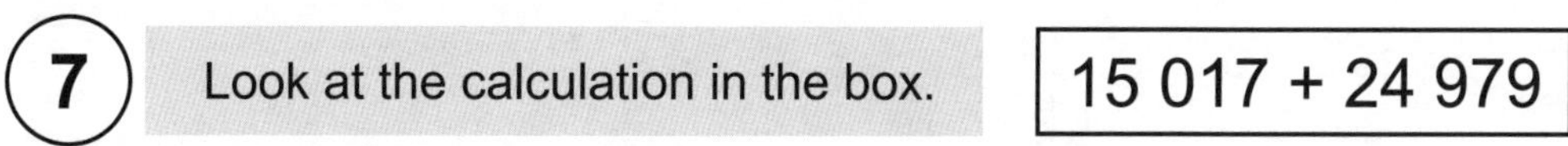

7 Look at the calculation in the box.

15 017 + 24 979

Work out the answer to the calculation.

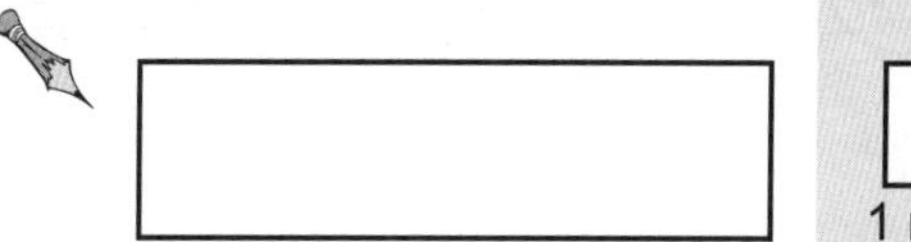

1 mark

Use rounding to write a calculation you could use to check your answer.

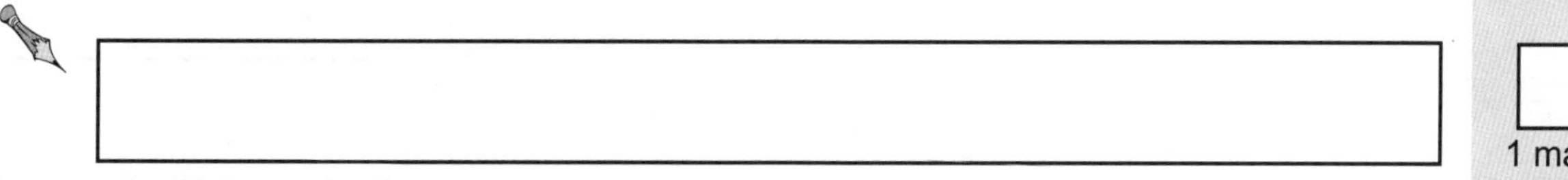

1 mark

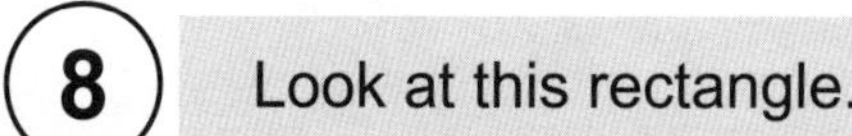

8 Look at this rectangle.

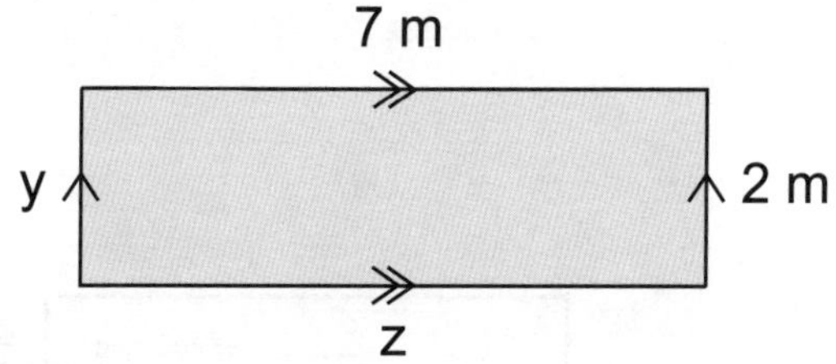

How much longer is side z than side y?

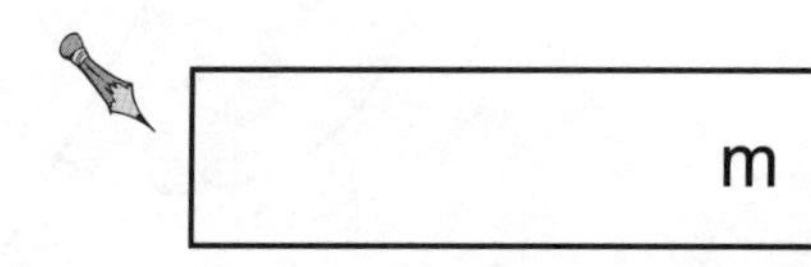

☐ m

1 mark

9 Convert 9800 g to kg.

kg

1 mark

10 A triangle is shown on the grid below.

Reflect the triangle in mirror line 1.
Then reflect **both** triangles in mirror line 2.

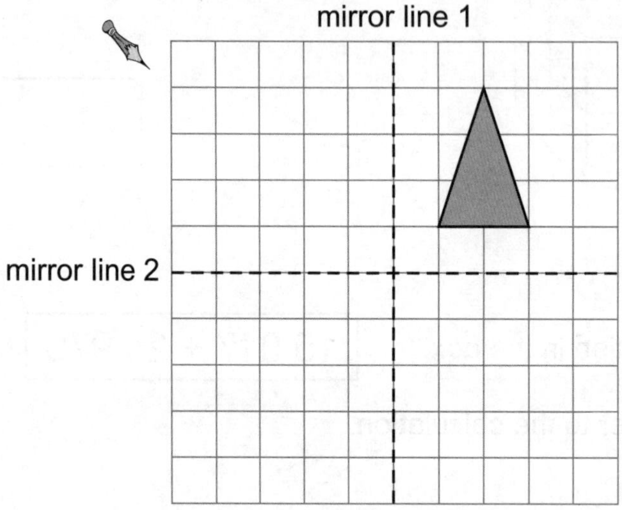

mirror line 1

mirror line 2

2 marks

11 Use a written method to work out 1012 × 36.

1 mark

12 Calculate the size of angle A.

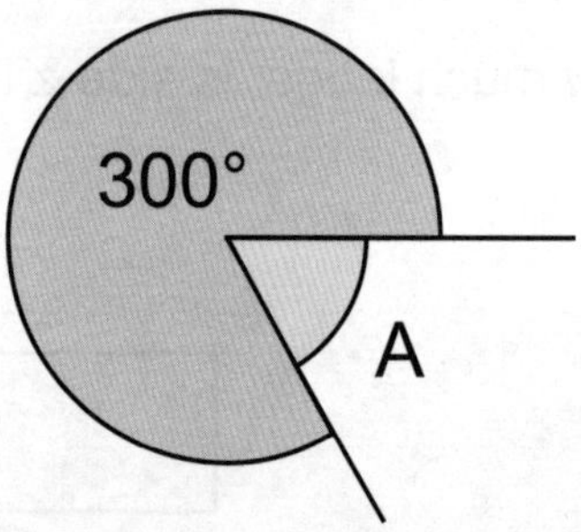

300°

A

°

1 mark

13 This line graph shows the cost of a cinema ticket over five years.

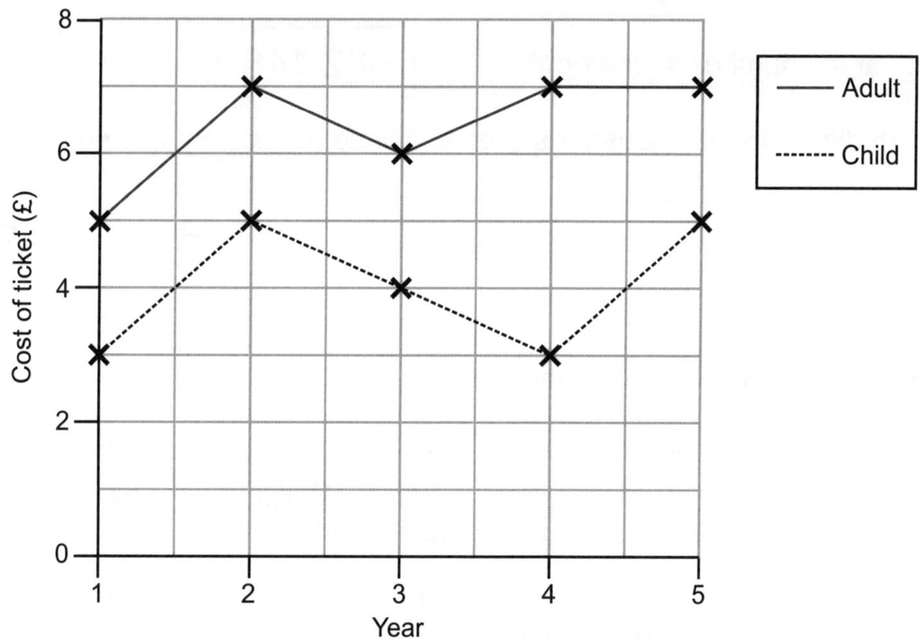

What was the total cost for one adult ticket and one child ticket in year 3?

£

1 mark

How much more did an adult ticket cost than a child ticket in year 5?

£

1 mark

14 Calculate:

$$\frac{3}{8} + \frac{1}{4} = \frac{\square}{8}$$

1 mark

15 Shreena owns two fishing rods.
Rod A is 200 cm long. Rod B is 5 feet long.

Use 1 m ≈ 3 feet to work out which fishing rod is **shorter**.
Show your working.

2 marks

Total

Place Value in Very Large Numbers

1 Look at the number on the right. **582 146**

Which digit is in the 'thousands' place? Circle the correct answer.

5 8 2 1 4 6

1 mark

2 Use partitioning to complete these sums.

702 090 = [ ] + 2000 + 90

1 mark

1 050 300 = 1 000 000 + [ ] + 300

1 mark

3 Write '<' or '>' in each of the boxes below.

987 300 [ ] 963 100   1 154 120 [ ] 1 172 200

2 marks

4 Write out 3 261 000 in words.

[ ]

1 mark

5 Put the following numbers in order. Start with the smallest.

2 320 900   1 412 100   1 234 600

[ ] [ ] [ ]

smallest ... largest

1 mark

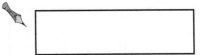

"I can read, write, order and compare numbers up to ten million."

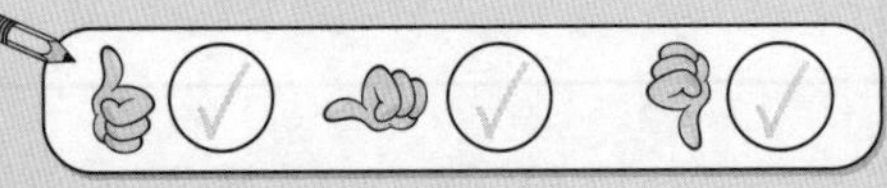

Rounding Whole Numbers

1 Circle the numbers below that round to 8000 to the nearest thousand.

7800 8100 8700

7200 8500 7500

1 mark

2 Round each of the numbers below to the nearest 10 000.

18 200 → ☐ 1 mark

154 000 → ☐ 1 mark

3 147 100 → ☐ 1 mark

3 There are 525 600 minutes in a normal year.

Round the number of minutes in a normal year to the nearest 100 000.

☐ 1 mark

4 Jenny scored 6 452 800 points on a pinball game.

Round the number of points that Jenny scored to the nearest million. ☐ 1 mark

Round the number of points that Jenny scored to the nearest thousand. ☐ 1 mark

"I can round any whole number."

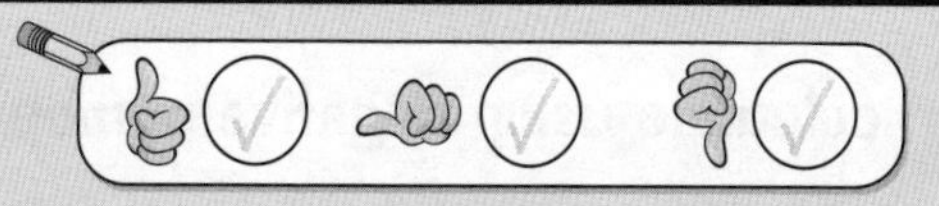

Calculating with Negative Numbers

Use the number line below to help you answer these questions.

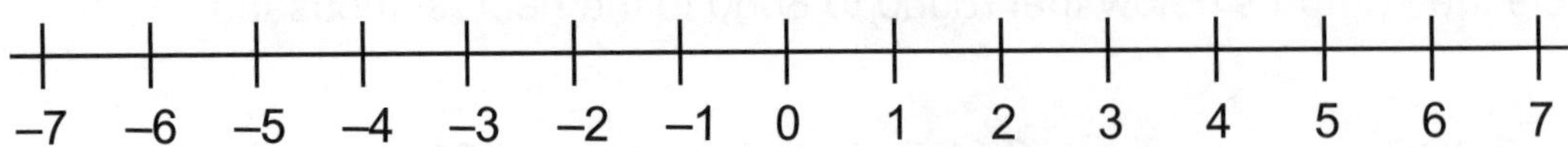

1 Write down the number you get to if you do the following.

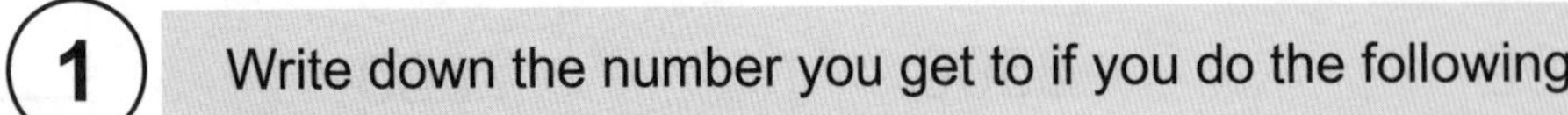

Start at –6 and count on 3.
Start at –1 and count back 4.

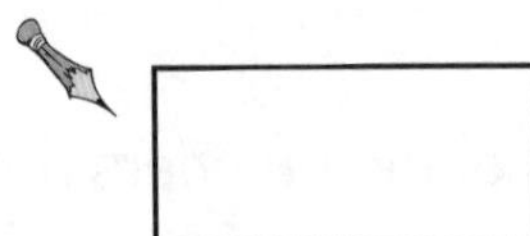

2 marks

2 Sammy starts at 3 and counts backwards in steps of 5.

Circle **two** numbers below that he will count.

–7 –6 –5 –4 –3 –2 –1

1 mark

3 Work out these additions.

–2 + 3 = ☐   –4 + 6 = ☐

2 marks

4 Work out these subtractions.

3 – 8 = ☐   1 – 5 = ☐

2 marks

5 Huw's garden was –5 °C in the morning and 3 °C in the afternoon.

What was the difference in temperature between the morning and afternoon?

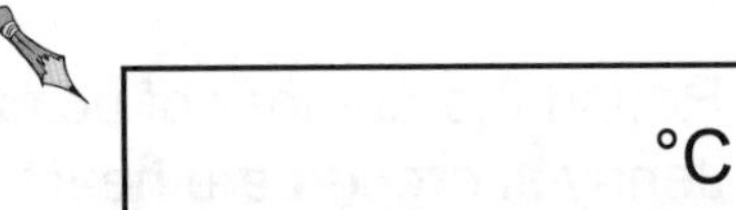

1 mark

"I can calculate using negative numbers."

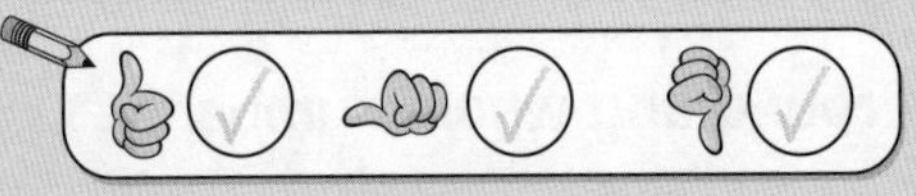

Solving Number Problems

1. Una is thinking of a number and describes it below.

My number has 4 millions, 6 ten thousands, 8 thousands, 3 tens and 7 ones.
What number is Una thinking of?

[ ] 1 mark

2. Some pupils took part in a maths competition. In this competition, you get a negative number of points if you answer incorrectly.

Jamal scored –5 points.

Marta scored 3 points less than Jamal.
How many points did Marta score?

points

1 mark

Katie scored 9 points more than Jamal.
How many points did Katie score?

points

1 mark

3. The values of three paintings are shown in the table on the right.

Painting	Value
Painting A	£3 527 000
Painting B	£3 540 000
Painting C	£3 493 000

Put the paintings in order.
Start with the painting with the lowest value.

Painting	Painting	Painting
lowest value		highest value

1 mark

What is the value of Painting C rounded to the nearest £1 000 000?

£

1 mark

What is the value of Painting A rounded to the nearest £10 000?

£

1 mark

"I can solve number problems."

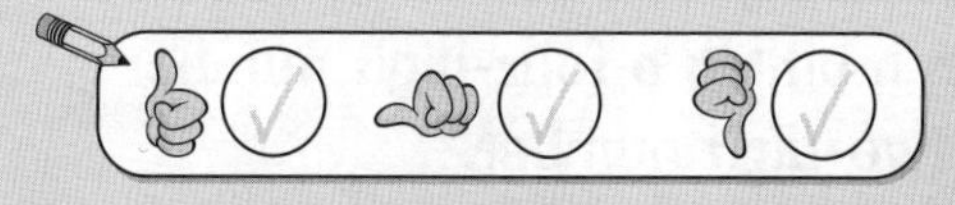

Written Multiplication

1 Calculate:

122 × 43

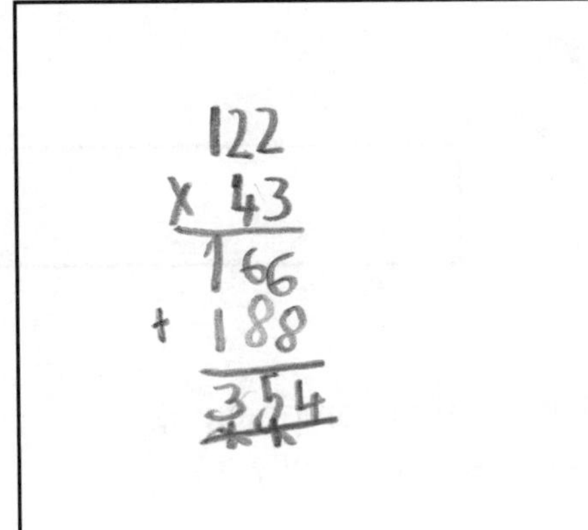

428 × 31

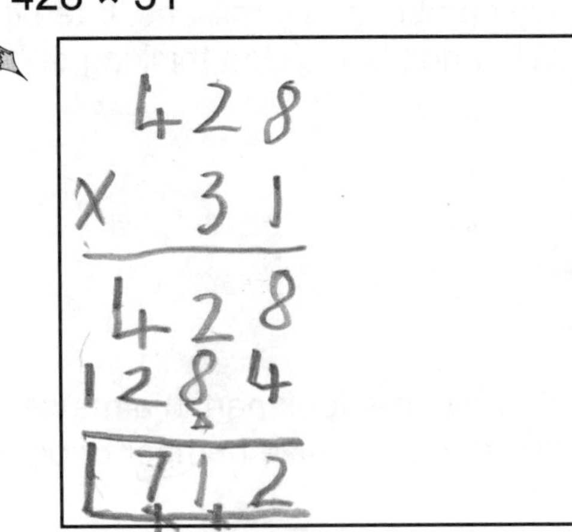

2 marks

2 Calculate:

1404 × 52

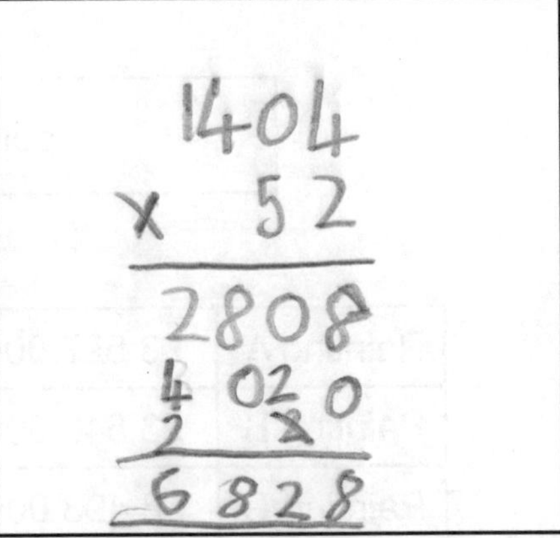

3314 × 26

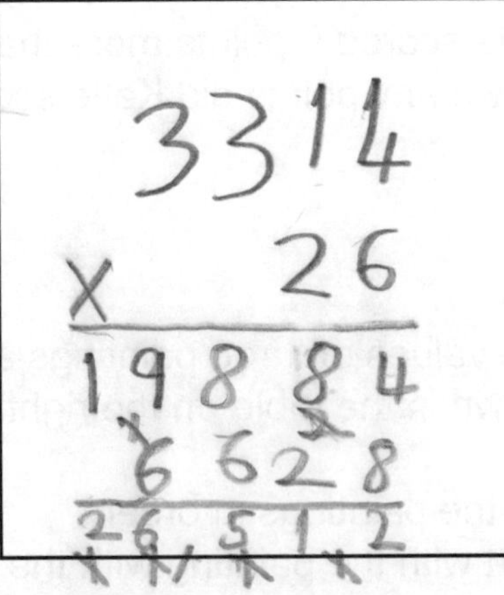

2 marks

3 A truck driver travels from Paris to Berlin and back again every week.
The total distance he travels each week is 2124 km.

How far will he travel in 52 weeks?

2124 X52 =110,448

110,448 km

2 marks

"I can multiply a four-digit number by a two-digit number."

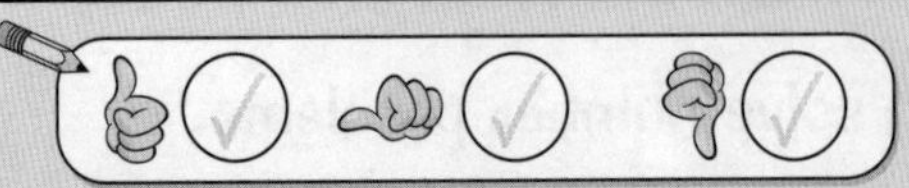

Written Division

1 Calculate:

516 ÷ 12

2373 ÷ 21

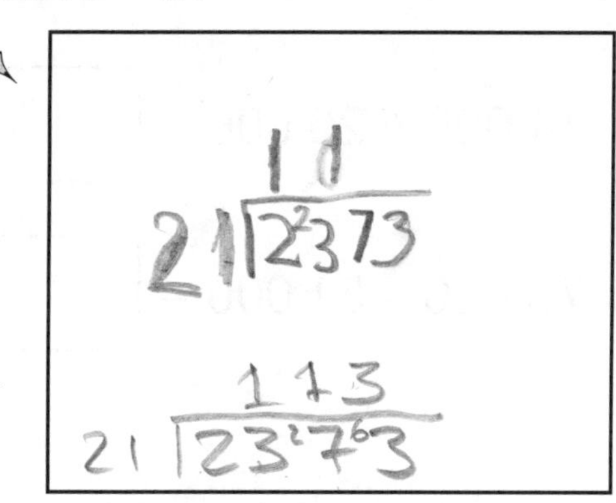

2 marks

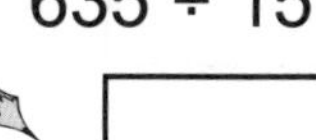

2 Work out these divisions. Write any remainders as whole numbers.

635 ÷ 15

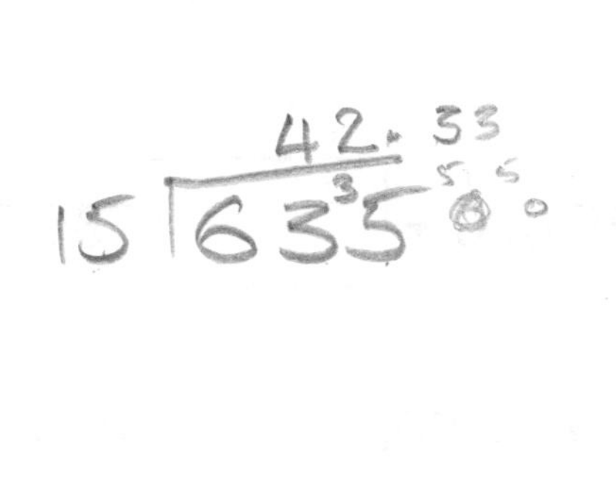

3309 ÷ 13

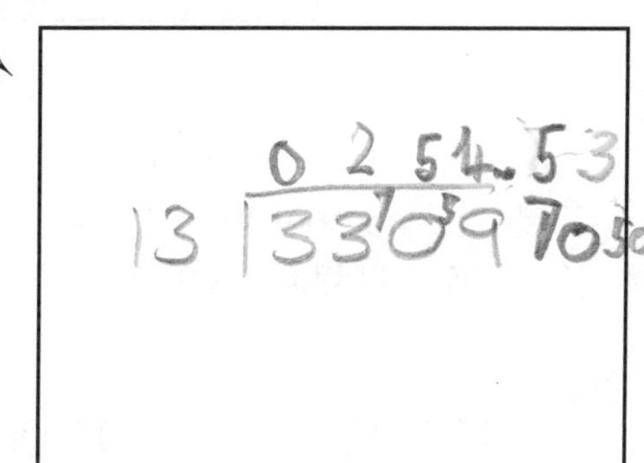

4 marks

3 A school has £2520 to spend on textbooks. Each textbook costs £11.

Calculate how many textbooks the school can afford to buy. Show your working.

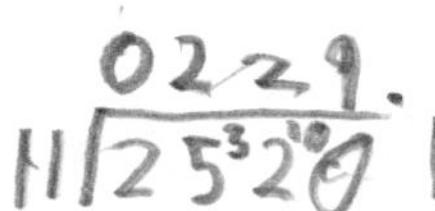

2 marks

How much money will they have left?

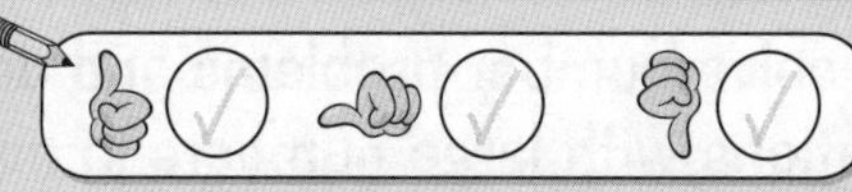

1 mark

"I can divide a four-digit number by a two-digit number and know what to do with remainders."

Mental Maths

This page is on **mental** maths, so you need to do these calculations in your head.

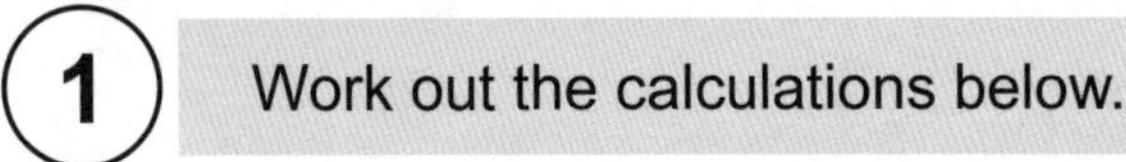

1. Work out the calculations below.

14 000 + 25 000 = ☐ (1 mark)

78 000 – 51 000 = ☐ (1 mark)

2. Work out these calculations.

8000 × 9 = ☐   3600 ÷ 6 = ☐ (2 marks)

3. Circle the number that should go in the empty box on the right.

325 000 + ☐ = 739 000

314 000   401 000   414 000   424 000 (1 mark)

4. A postman can visit 900 houses in one day.

How many houses can he visit in 7 days?

☐ houses (1 mark)

5. A baker makes bread rolls in batches of 40.

On Monday, he made a total of 2800 bread rolls.
How many batches did he make?

☐ batches (1 mark)

"I can solve number problems and do calculations with large numbers in my head."

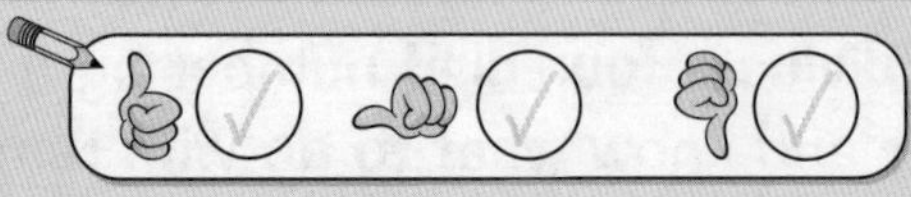

Estimating and Checking

1 Which calculation is best to estimate the value of 182 ÷ 29.7?

Circle the correct answer.

100 ÷ 20   180 ÷ 30   100 ÷ 30   180 ÷ 20

1 mark

Use your answer to estimate the value of 182 ÷ 29.7

1 mark

2 Selma is working out 23 041 – 5954.

By rounding to the nearest thousand, write down a calculation she could do to estimate the answer.

1 mark

3 At Gathertown United's last three football matches there were 49 574 fans, 60 247 fans and 69 399 fans.

Estimate the total number of fans at their last three matches.

fans

1 mark

4 Amelia works out that 87.5 × 28 = 1450.

Use rounding to check her answer. Is she right? Explain your answer.

2 marks

"I can estimate to check the answer of a calculation."

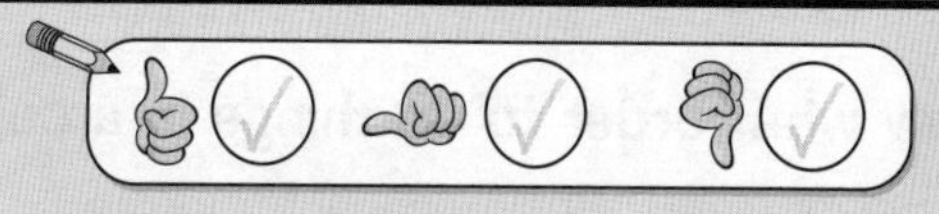

BODMAS

1 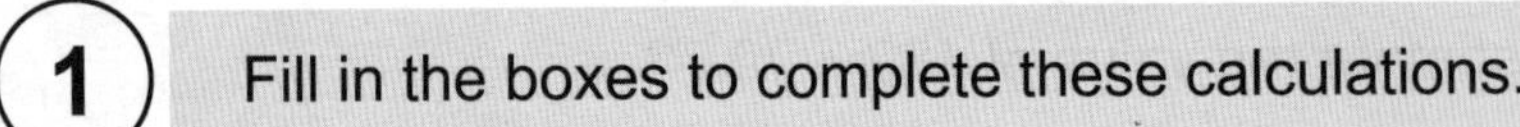

Fill in the boxes to complete these calculations.

10 – (9 ÷ 3) = 10 – ☐ = ☐

1 mark

(6 – 4) × 5 = ☐ × 5 = ☐

1 mark

2 Use the rules of BODMAS to work out the following calculations.

7 + 18 ÷ 3 = ☐ 9 – 4 × 2 = ☐

2 marks

3 Chen works out that 8 + 2 × 9 = 90.

Is Chen correct? Explain your answer.

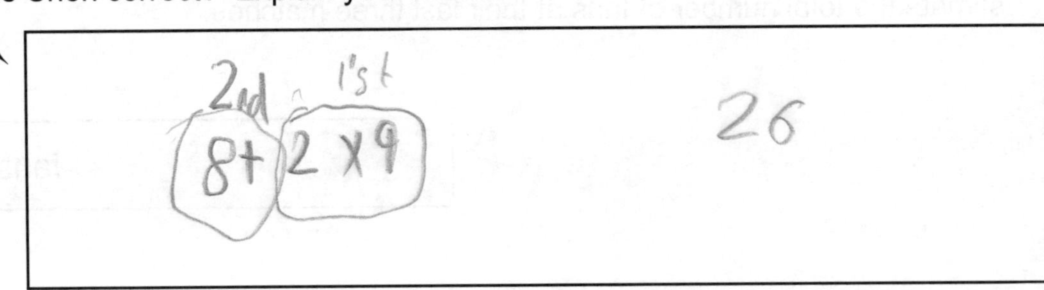

2 marks

4 Fill in the missing numbers to complete these calculations.

7 × (4 + ☐) = 49

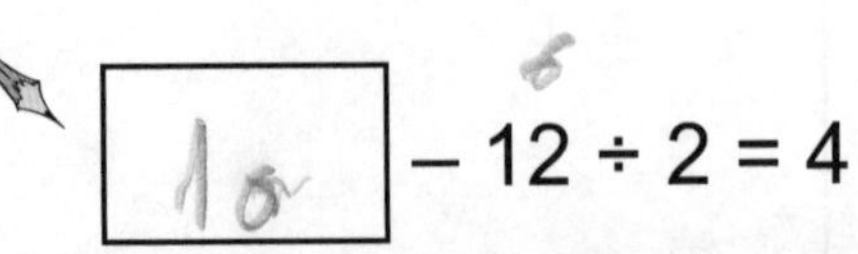

☐ – 12 ÷ 2 = 4

2 marks

"I know what order to do things in a calculation."

Multiples, Factors and Primes

1 Look at the numbers below.

7 26 28 15 43

18 81 56 77

Which **two** of the numbers are prime numbers? ___ and ___ 1 mark

Circle all of the numbers that have a factor of 7. 1 mark

2 Put a tick in the box below numbers that are common multiples of 5 and 6.

12	30	45	60	80
☐	☐	☐	☐	☐

1 mark

3 Write down all of the common factors of 20 and 50.

1 mark

4 How many numbers less than 50 are common multiples of 7 and 3?

1 mark

5 Write down all of the prime common factors of 42 and 60.

1 mark

"I know how to find common multiples, common factors and prime numbers."

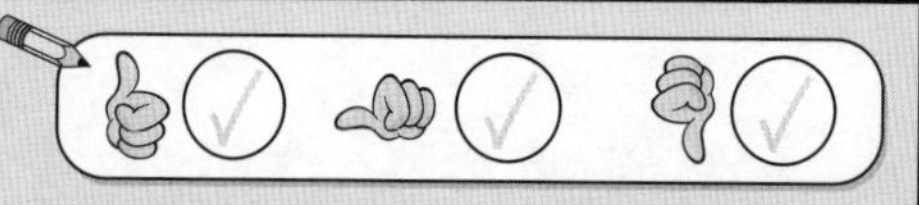

Solving Calculation Problems

1 Mrs Peacock has 5 packs of pens. Each pack contains 12 pens. She hands out 25 pens to her class.

Circle the calculation which will tell you how many pens she has left.

$5 \times 12 + 25$ $25 - 5 \times 12$ $5 \times 12 - 25$

1 mark

How many pens will Mrs Peacock have left?

pens

1 mark

2 There are 5 classrooms in a school. Each classroom has 8 tables, with 4 pupils sitting around each table.

Circle the calculation which will tell you how many pupils are at the school.

$5 \times 8 \times 4$ $5 \times 8 + 4$ $5 + 8 \times 4$

1 mark

How many pupils are there at the school?

pupils

1 mark

3 Kyle has picked 58 blackberries and Paul has picked 92. They share the blackberries equally between them.

How many blackberries does each person get?

blackberries

1 mark

Solving Calculation Problems

4 A fairground ride has 16 carts. 10 of the carts have 4 people in them and 6 of the carts have 3 people in them.

If half the people get off, how many are left on the ride?

[ ] people

1 mark

5 There are 90 pupils on a school trip. They are split into seven groups. Three of the groups each have 14 pupils in them. The other four groups all contain the same number of pupils.

How many pupils are in each of the other four groups?

[ ] pupils

1 mark

6 Dan, Raj and Sky scored a total of 180 points in an archery competition. Dan scored 20 points and Raj scored 3 times as many points as Dan.

How many more points did Sky score than Dan?

[ ] points

1 mark

"I can work out what calculations I need to use to solve a problem."

Simplifying Fractions

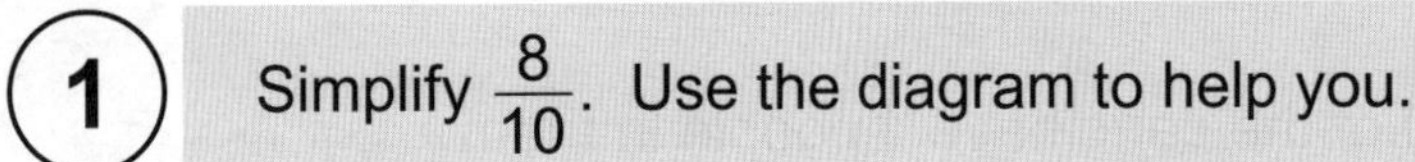

1 Simplify $\frac{8}{10}$. Use the diagram to help you.

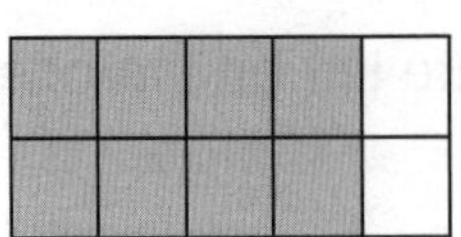

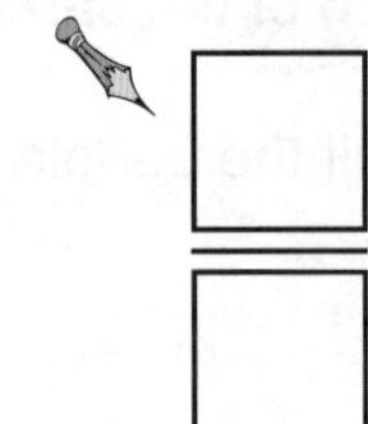

1 mark

2 Draw lines to match the fractions on the top with an equivalent fraction underneath.

One has been done for you.

$\frac{9}{12}$ $\frac{6}{10}$ $\frac{18}{20}$ $\frac{5}{15}$

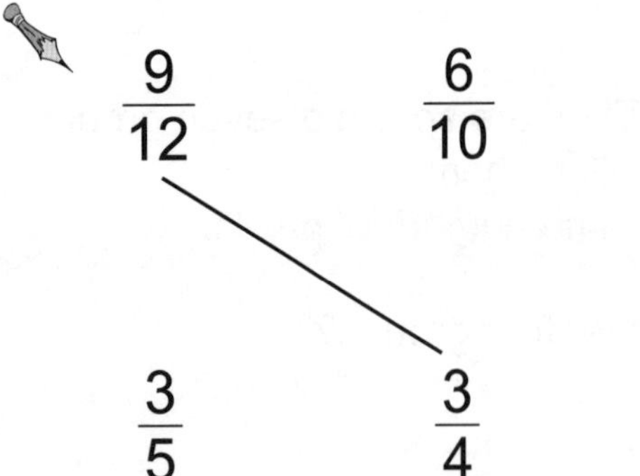

$\frac{3}{5}$ $\frac{3}{4}$ $\frac{1}{3}$ $\frac{9}{10}$

1 mark

3 Look at the fractions below.

Circle the **two** fractions that **cannot** be simplified.

$\frac{2}{10}$ $\frac{7}{12}$ $\frac{4}{5}$ $\frac{3}{9}$

1 mark

4 Rewrite the fractions $\frac{1}{4}$ and $\frac{2}{3}$ so that they have the same denominator.

$\frac{1}{4}$ = $\frac{\square}{\square}$ $\frac{2}{3}$ = $\frac{\square}{\square}$

2 marks

"I can simplify fractions. I can write equivalent fractions with the same denominator."

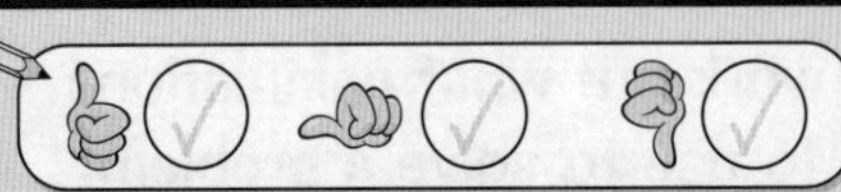

Ordering Fractions

1 Fill in the missing numbers.

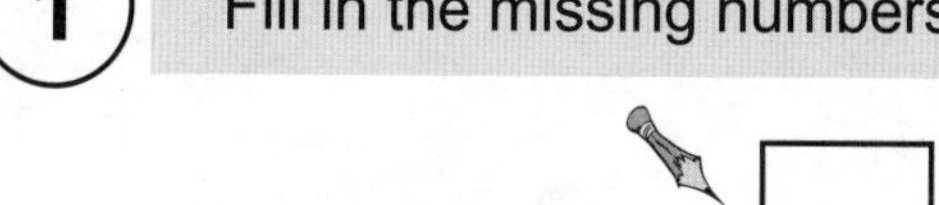

$\frac{6}{9} = \frac{\square}{3}$ $\frac{2}{6} = \frac{\square}{3}$

1 mark

Use your answers to circle the larger fraction.  $\frac{6}{9}$ $\frac{2}{6}$

1 mark

2 Write these fractions so they have a common denominator of 20.

$\frac{1}{4} = \frac{\square}{20}$ $\frac{7}{10} = \frac{\square}{20}$ $\frac{2}{5} = \frac{\square}{20}$

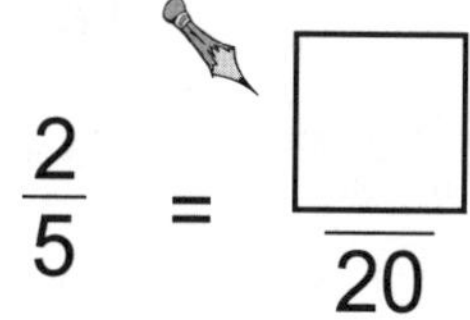

1 mark

Use your answers to write $\frac{1}{4}$, $\frac{7}{10}$ and $\frac{2}{5}$ in order, starting with the smallest.

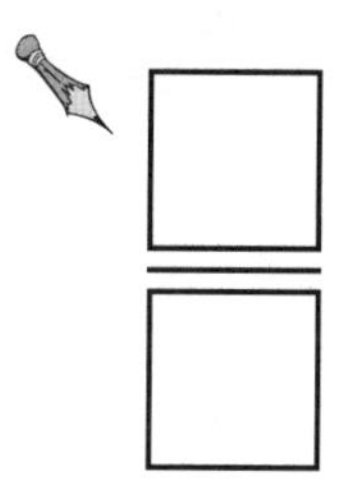

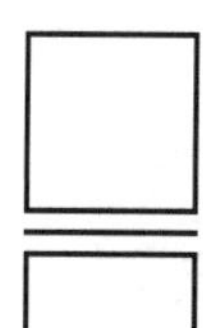

smallest largest

1 mark

3 Put the fractions in order. Start with the largest.

$\frac{8}{5}$ $1\frac{1}{5}$ $\frac{11}{5}$

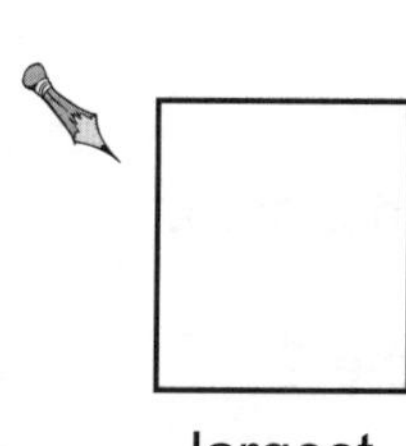

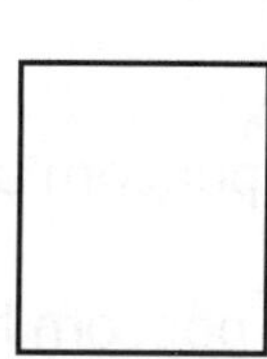

largest smallest

1 mark

"I can compare and order fractions, including fractions greater than 1."

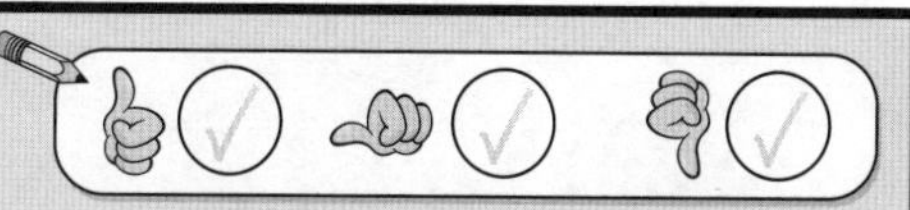

Adding and Subtracting Fractions

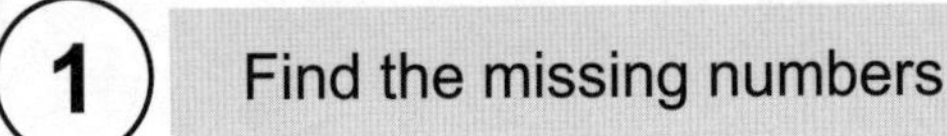

1 Find the missing numbers:

$\frac{2}{5} + \frac{3}{10} = \frac{\square}{10}$ $\frac{7}{8} - \frac{1}{4} = \frac{\square}{8}$

2 marks

2 Work out and simplify:

$\frac{5}{12} + \frac{1}{4} = \frac{\square}{12} = \frac{\square}{3}$

1 mark

$\frac{2}{3} - \frac{1}{6} = \frac{\square}{6} = \frac{\square}{2}$

1 mark

3 What is $\frac{5}{8} + \frac{3}{2}$?

Circle the correct answer.

$\frac{10}{8}$ $\frac{17}{8}$ $\frac{13}{8}$

1 mark

4 Keira and Josh are sharing some popcorn.

Keira eats $\frac{1}{3}$ of the popcorn and Josh eats $\frac{5}{9}$ of the popcorn.

What fraction of the popcorn have they eaten altogether?

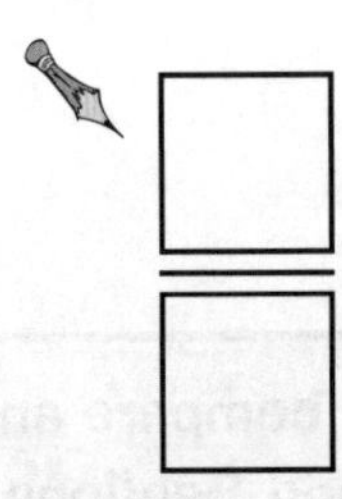

1 mark

Adding and Subtracting Fractions

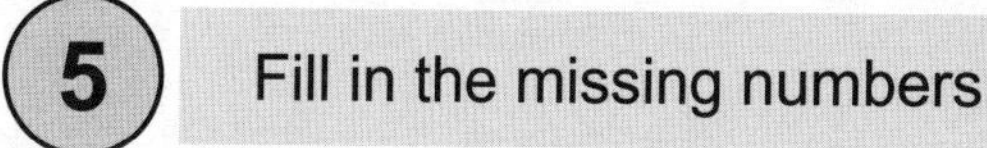

5 Fill in the missing numbers:

$$\frac{1}{2} + \frac{2}{5} = \frac{\square}{10} + \frac{\square}{10} = \frac{\square}{10}$$

2 marks

$$\frac{3}{4} - \frac{3}{5} = \frac{\square}{20} - \frac{\square}{20} = \frac{\square}{20}$$

2 marks

6 Fill in the missing box.

$$1\frac{2}{3} + \frac{2}{9} = 1\frac{\square}{9}$$

1 mark

7 Dylan and Allie are throwing water balloons.

Dylan throws $\frac{7}{12}$ of the water balloons.

Allie throws $\frac{1}{3}$ of the water balloons.

What fraction of the water balloons have **not** been thrown?

1 mark

8 Work out $\frac{3}{5} + \frac{1}{6}$.

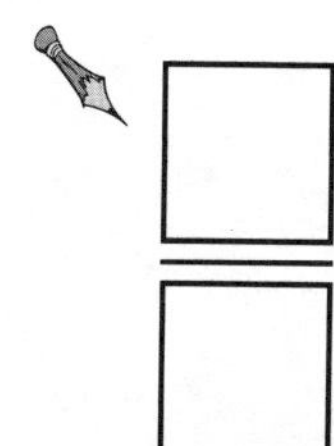

1 mark

"I can add and subtract fractions by using a common denominator."

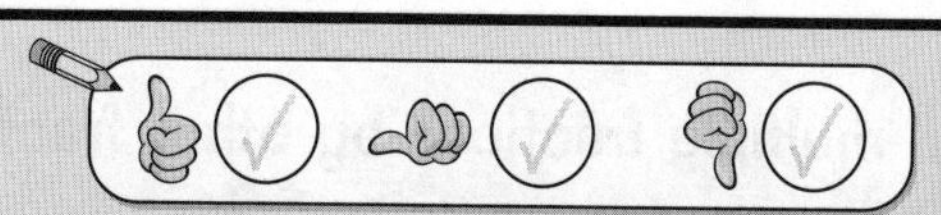

Multiplying Fractions

1 Work out:

$\frac{1}{2} \times \frac{1}{5} = \frac{\square}{\square}$ $\frac{1}{3} \times \frac{1}{6} = \frac{\square}{\square}$

2 marks

$\frac{3}{5} \times \frac{1}{4} = \frac{\square}{\square}$ $\frac{1}{2} \times \frac{5}{6} = \frac{\square}{\square}$

2 marks

2 Work out $\frac{1}{2} \times \frac{4}{5}$.

Circle the answer in its simplest form.

$\frac{6}{10}$ $\frac{2}{5}$ $\frac{4}{10}$ $\frac{3}{5}$

1 mark

3 Calculate $\frac{2}{3} \times \frac{8}{10}$. Simplify your answer.

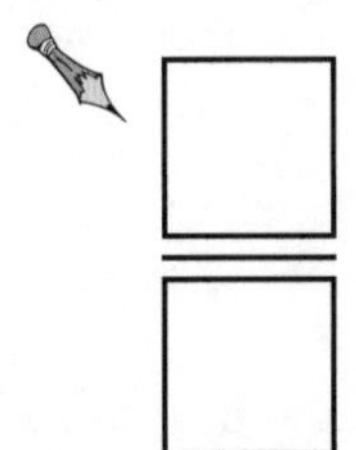

1 mark

"I can multiply fractions by other fractions."

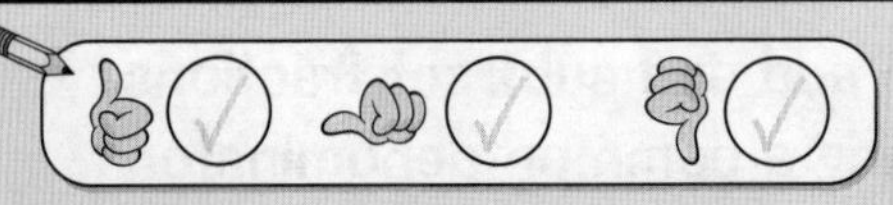

Dividing Fractions by Whole Numbers

1 Work out:

$\frac{1}{2} \div 3 = \frac{\square}{\square}$ $\frac{1}{4} \div 5 = \frac{\square}{\square}$

2 marks

2 Draw lines to match the calculation with the correct answer.

$\frac{2}{3} \div 5$	$\frac{3}{15}$
$\frac{3}{5} \div 3$	$\frac{3}{16}$
$\frac{3}{4} \div 4$	$\frac{2}{15}$

1 mark

3 What is $\frac{6}{15} \div 4$? Simplify your answer.

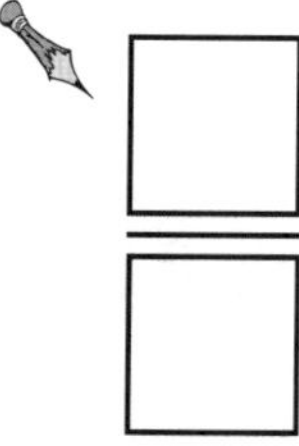

1 mark

4 Lucy has $\frac{1}{2}$ of a pie left over. She shares it between 6 people.

What fraction of the whole pie does each person get?

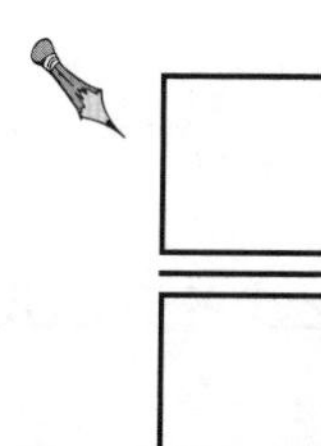

1 mark

"I can divide fractions by whole numbers."

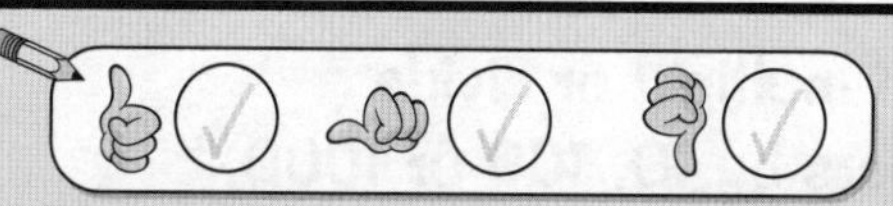

Multiplying or Dividing by 10, 100 or 1000

1 Draw lines to match each number to the value of the underlined digit.

$2.4\underline{5}$	five thousandths
$0.11\underline{5}$	five tenths
$3.\underline{5}07$	five hundredths

2 marks

2 Write × or ÷ in the boxes to make the calculations correct.

63.1 ☐ 100 = 6310   42 ☐ 1000 = 0.042

2 marks

3 Calculate:

4.21 ÷ 10

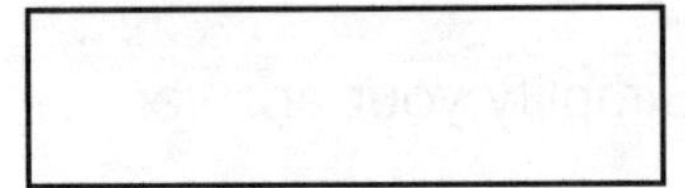

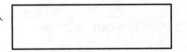

1 mark

1.845 × 100

1 mark

4 What is the value of the underlined digit after each multiplication?

$0.9\underline{2}$ × 10

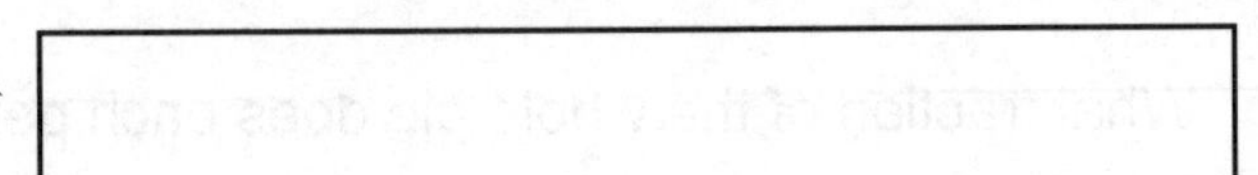

1 mark

$1.\underline{2}3$ × 1000

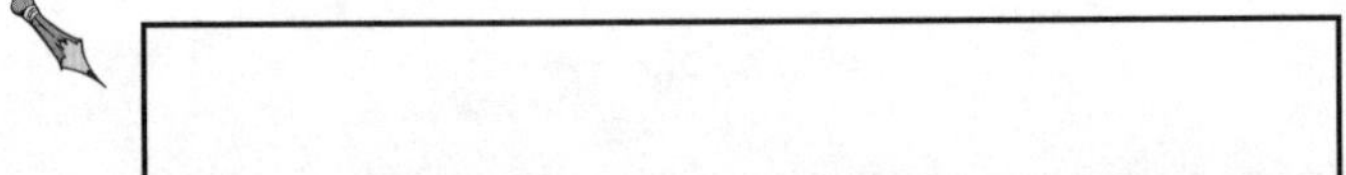

1 mark

"I can multiply or divide numbers by 10, 100 or 1000."

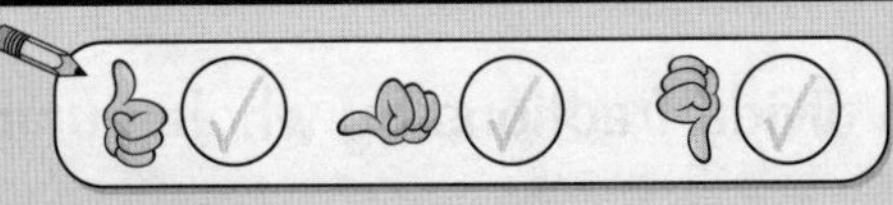

Multiplying with Decimals

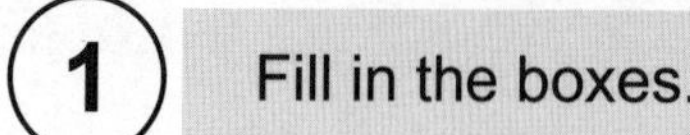

1 Fill in the boxes.

4 × 3 = 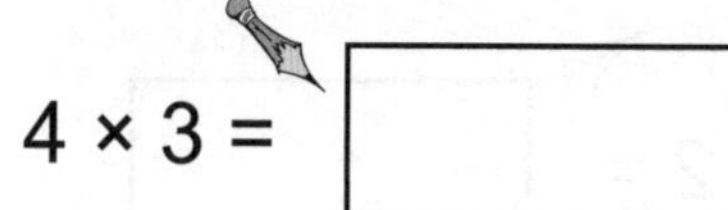

0.4 × 3 =

1 mark

2 Calculate:

0.2 × 7

0.8 × 6

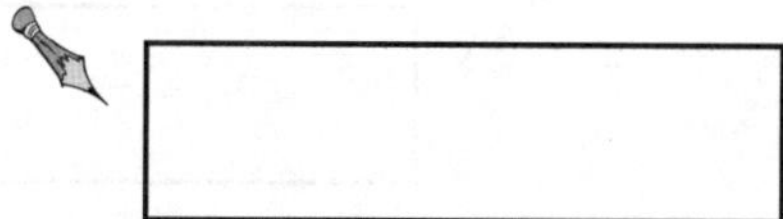

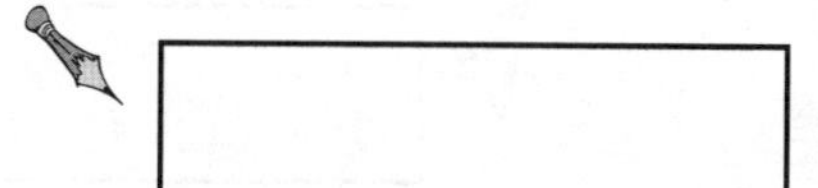

2 marks

3 Circle the correct answer to each multiplication.

1.3 × 2  2.6 26 13

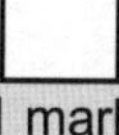

1 mark

2.2 × 4 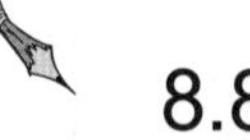 8.8 6.6 12.8

1 mark

0.06 × 6 0.12 0.36 0.036

1 mark

4 What is 0.89 × 5?

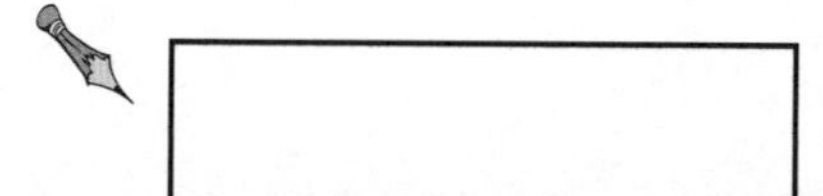

1 mark

"I can multiply decimal numbers by whole numbers."

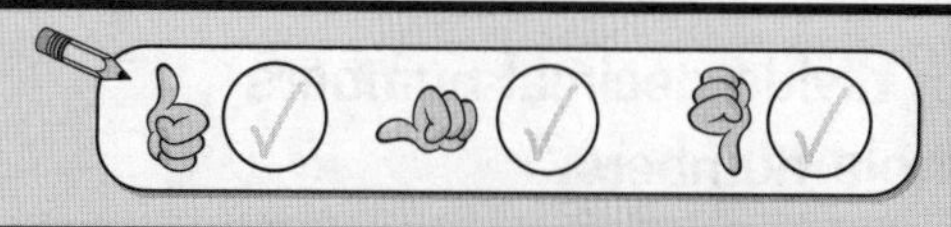

Dividing with Decimals

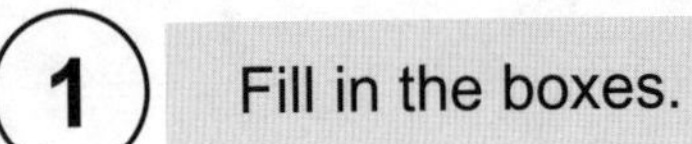

1 Fill in the boxes.

68 ÷ 2 = ☐ 6.8 ÷ 2 = ☐

1 mark

2 Calculate:

3.3 ÷ 3

6.3 ÷ 7

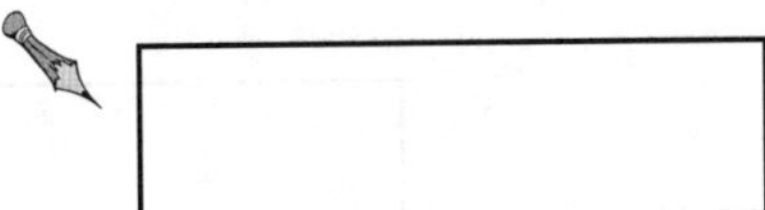

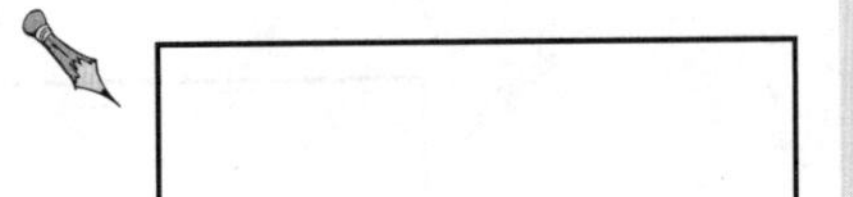

2 marks

3 Use a written method to work out these divisions:

21.6 ÷ 6

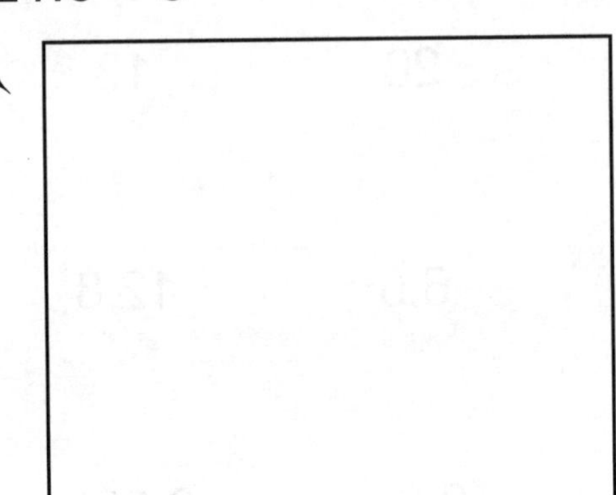

1.53 ÷ 9

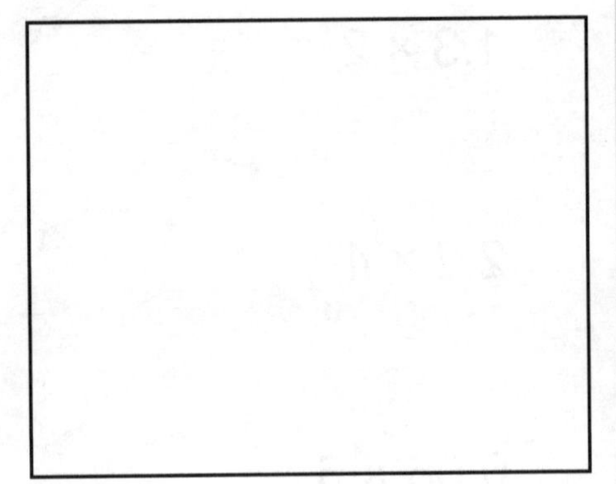

2 marks

4 2.4 litres of soup is shared equally between 4 bowls.

How much soup is there in each bowl?

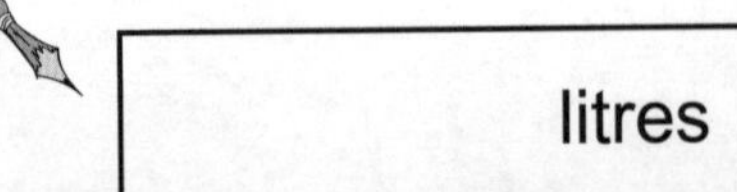

1 mark

"I can divide decimal numbers by whole numbers."

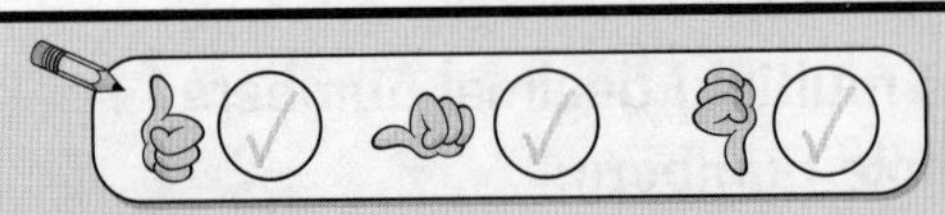

Rounding Decimals

1 Round the numbers on these cards to 1 decimal place.

2.11 → [ ]   3.55 → [ ]

2 marks

2 Round to 1 decimal place:

5.938 [ ]   1.062 [ ]

2 marks

3 Round to 2 decimal places:

3.653 [ ]   2.906 [ ]

2 marks

4 A roll of wallpaper is 1.41 m long.
A decorator uses **two** rolls to cover a wall.

What is the total length of wallpaper used?
Give your answer to 1 decimal place.

[ ] m

1 mark

5 A bag of gravel weighs 8.0 kg to the nearest 1 decimal place.

Which of these could be the **exact** weight of the bag?
Circle the correct answer.

7.94 kg   7.09 kg   8.05 kg   7.96 kg

1 mark

"I can round decimal numbers
to a given number of decimal places."

Fractions, Decimals and Percentages

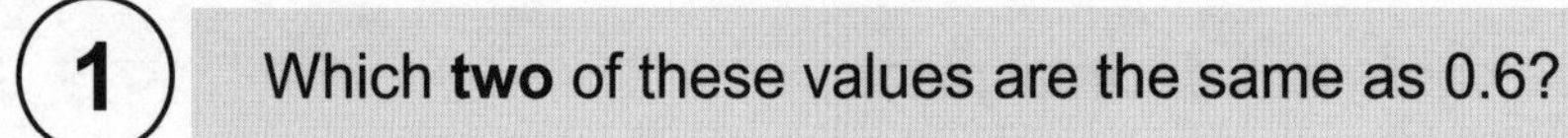

1 Which **two** of these values are the same as 0.6?

Circle the correct answers.

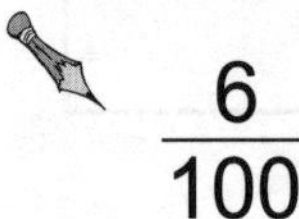

$\frac{6}{100}$ 6% $\frac{6}{10}$ $\frac{1}{6}$ 60%

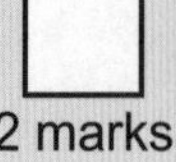

2 marks

2 Find the missing numbers below.

$0.15 = \frac{\square}{100} = \square\,\%$

1 mark

$\frac{20}{25} = \frac{\square}{100} = \square\,\%$

1 mark

3 Draw lines to match the equivalent amounts.

The first one has been done for you.

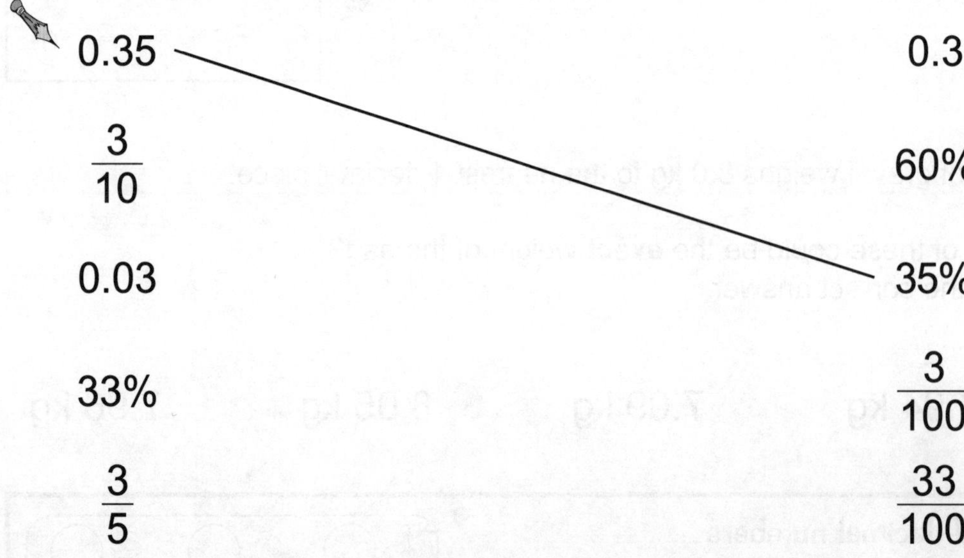

0.35	0.3
$\frac{3}{10}$	60%
0.03	35%
33%	$\frac{3}{100}$
$\frac{3}{5}$	$\frac{33}{100}$

2 marks

Fractions, Decimals and Percentages

4 Complete the table to show the equivalent forms of these values.

Write the fractions in their simplest form.

Decimal	Percentage	Fraction
0.2		
	70%	
		$\frac{3}{20}$

3 marks

5 Use the instructions below to convert $\frac{1}{8}$ to a decimal:

Step 1: Work out 1000 ÷ 8
Step 2: Divide your answer by 1000

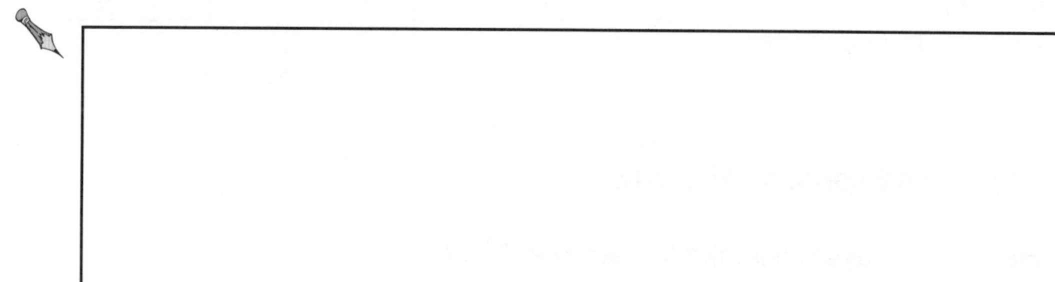

2 marks

6 Tomasz has climbed 45% of the way up a mountain.

Selena has climbed $\frac{30}{50}$ of the way up the same mountain.

Who has climbed the furthest? Explain your answer.

2 marks

"I can convert fractions to decimals by dividing. I can convert between fractions, decimals and percentages."

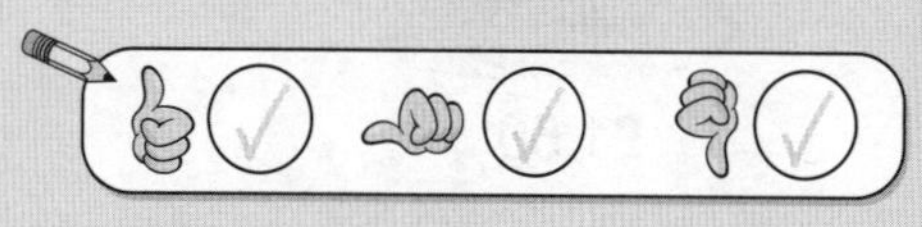

Relative Sizes

1 3 tomatoes in a greenhouse turn ripe every week.

How many tomatoes will be ripe after 7 weeks?
Use the number lines to help you.

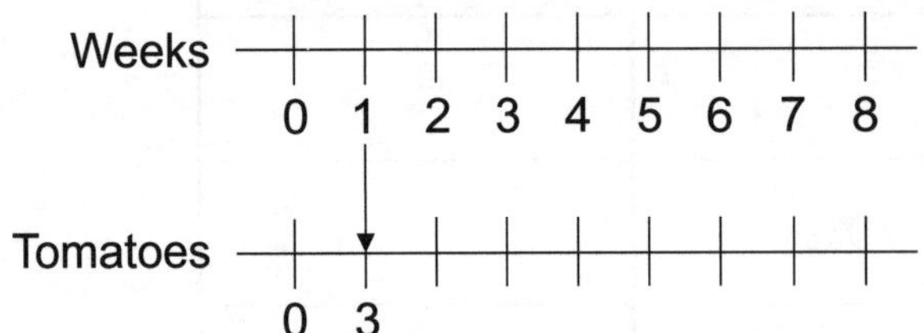

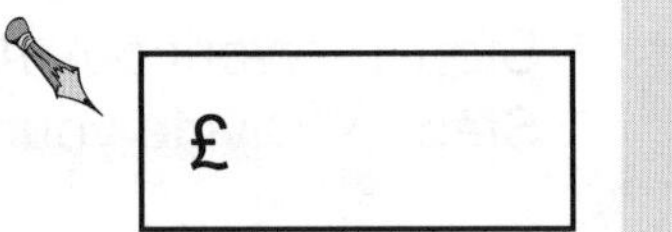

tomatoes

1 mark

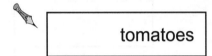

2 A dolphin rubber costs 50p. How much will 4 rubbers cost?

Give your answer in pounds.

50p

£

1 mark

3 Laura eats 6 carrot sticks a day.

How many days will it take for her to eat 24 carrot sticks?
Use the number lines to help you.

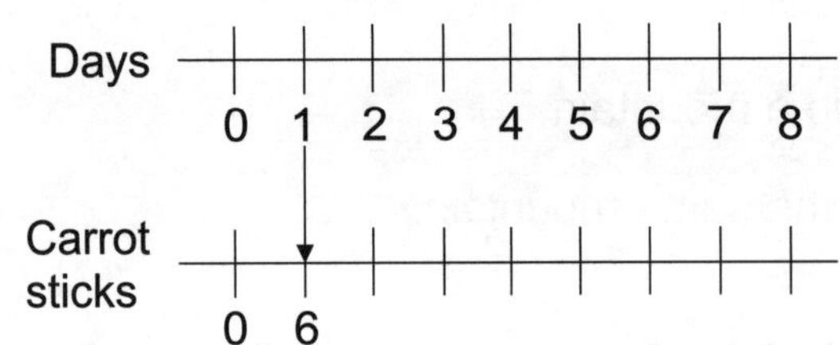

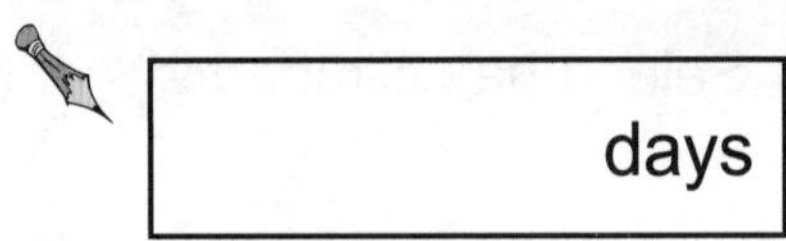

days

1 mark

4 A bag of 5 oranges costs £1.50. How much does 1 orange cost?

Give your answer in pence.

£1.50

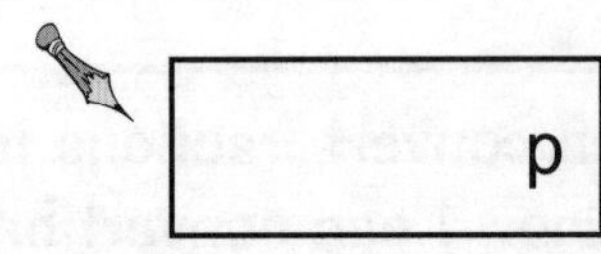

p

1 mark

Relative Sizes

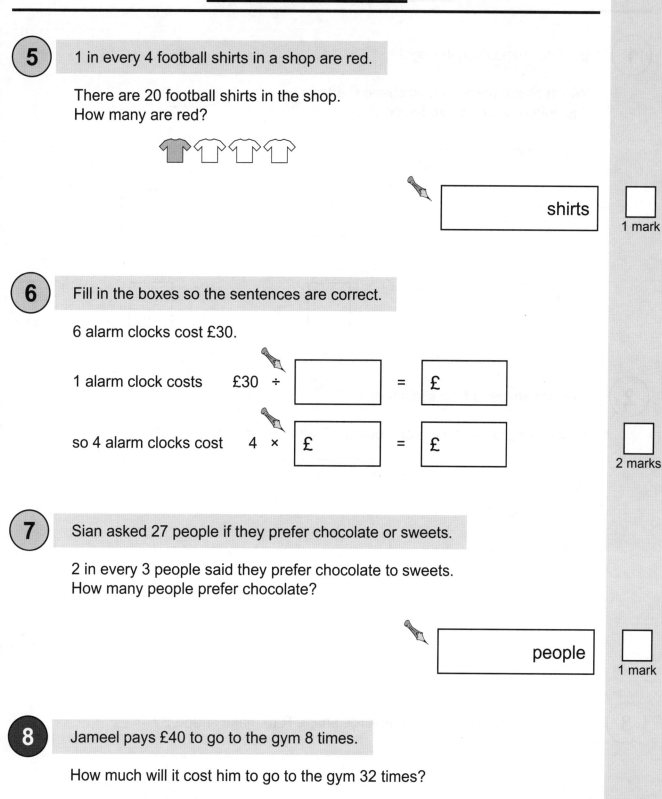

5 1 in every 4 football shirts in a shop are red.

There are 20 football shirts in the shop.
How many are red?

[ ] shirts

1 mark

6 Fill in the boxes so the sentences are correct.

6 alarm clocks cost £30.

1 alarm clock costs £30 ÷ [ ] = £ [ ]

so 4 alarm clocks cost 4 × £ [ ] = £ [ ]

2 marks

7 Sian asked 27 people if they prefer chocolate or sweets.

2 in every 3 people said they prefer chocolate to sweets.
How many people prefer chocolate?

[ ] people

1 mark

8 Jameel pays £40 to go to the gym 8 times.

How much will it cost him to go to the gym 32 times?

£ [ ]

1 mark

"I can solve problems that are to do with the relative sizes of two amounts."

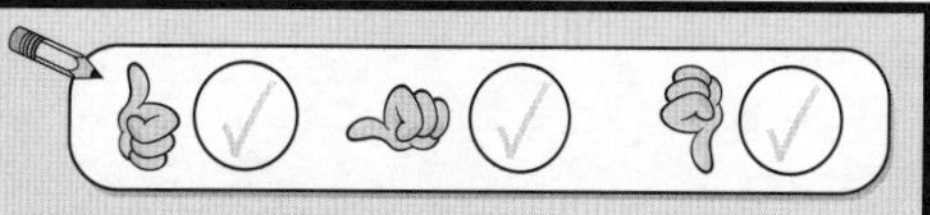

Scale Factors

1 Look at shape P on the right.

P

Which shape below shows shape P after it is enlarged by a scale factor of 3?

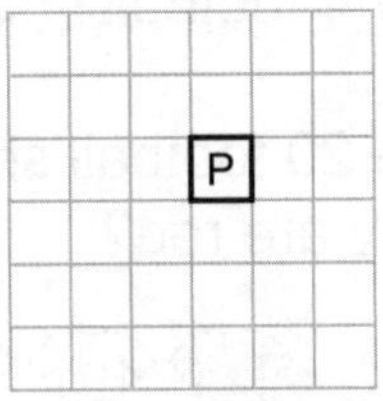

Tick the correct answer.

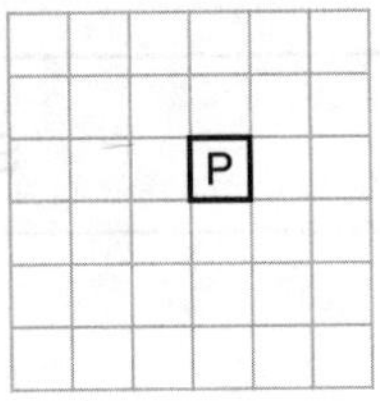

P

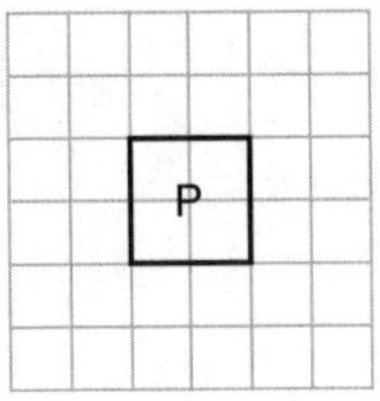

P

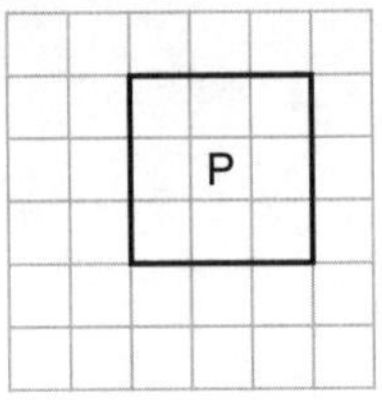

P

1 mark

2 Enlarge shape Q by a scale factor of 2.

Draw your answer on the grid below. Start from point A.

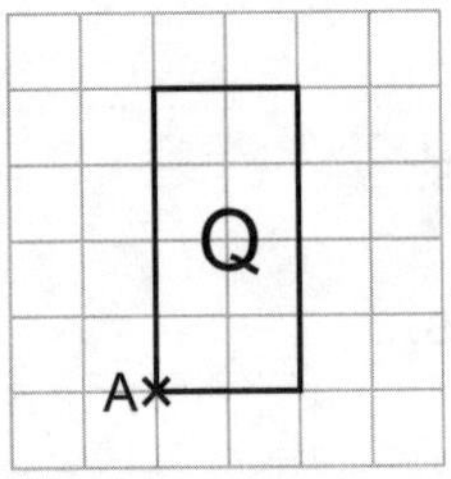

Q

A×

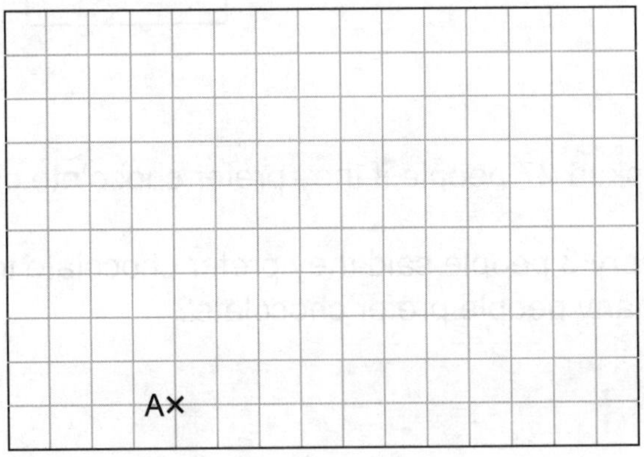

A×

1 mark

3 What scale factor is used to enlarge shape R to make shape S?

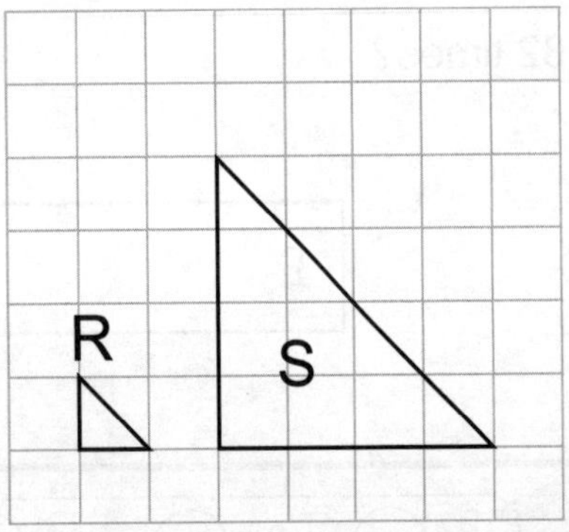

R

S

1 mark

Scale Factors

4 Enlarge shape W by a scale factor of 5.

Draw your answer on the grid below. Start from point A.

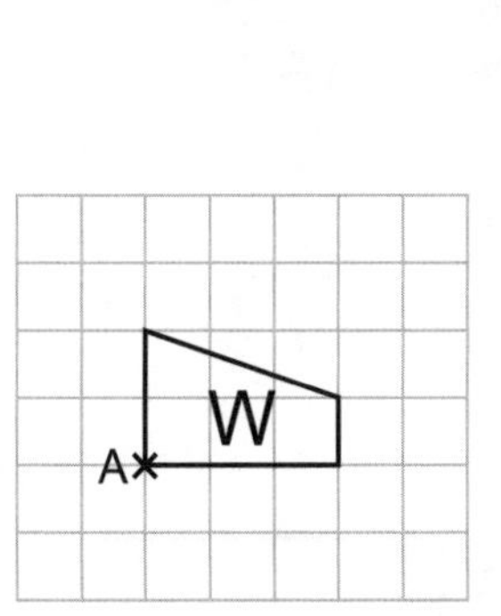

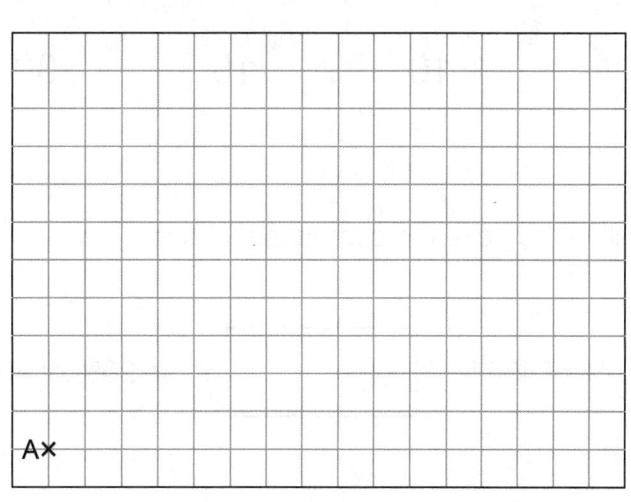

1 mark

5 Work out the scale factors used to enlarge shape A to make shape B.

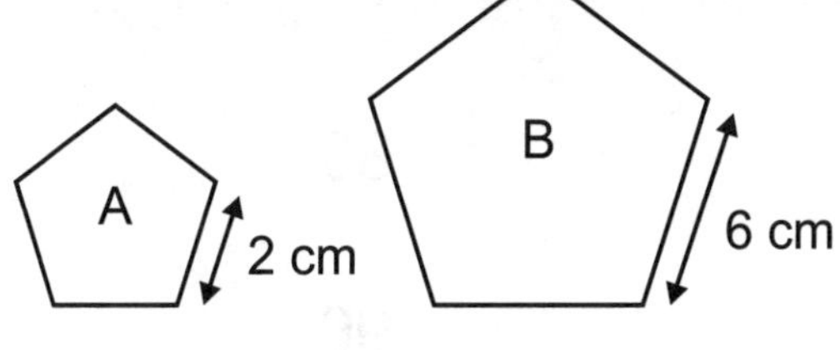

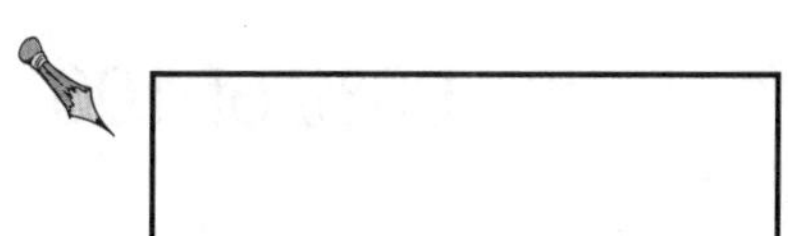

1 mark

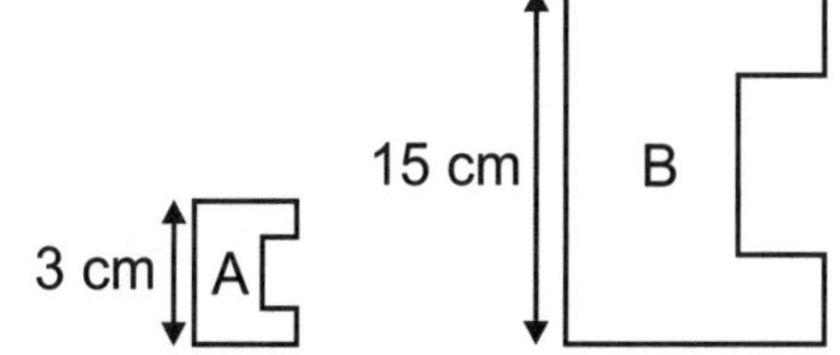

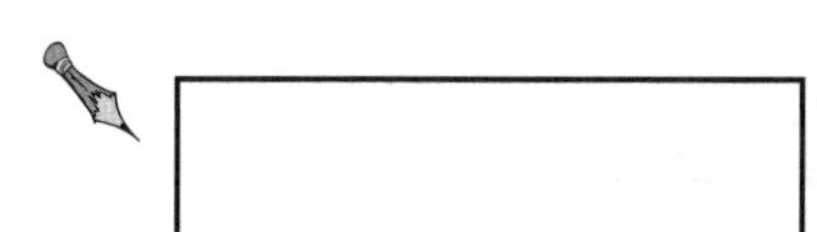

1 mark

6 Shape X is enlarged by a scale factor of 10 to make shape Y.

What is the length of side a?

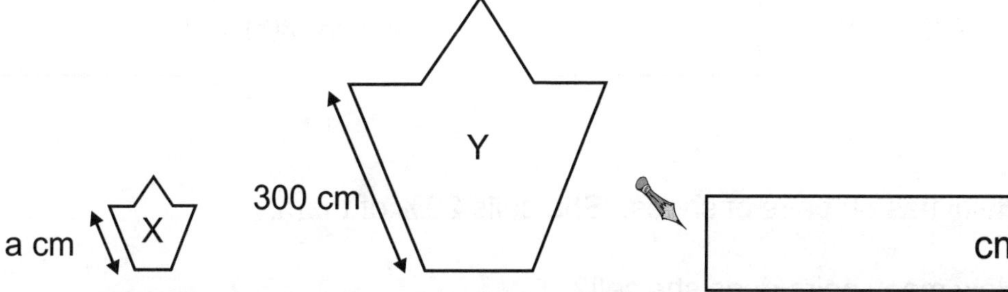

cm

1 mark

"I can enlarge a shape by a scale factor and I can find the scale factor of an enlarged shape."

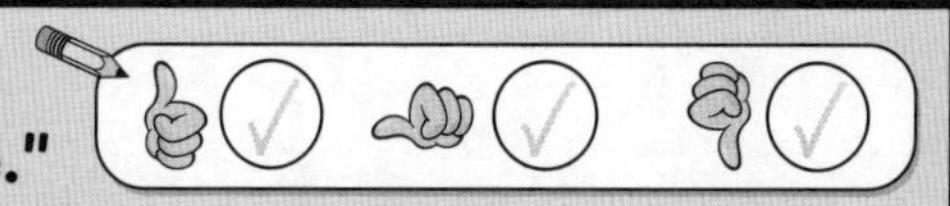

Percentages of Amounts

1 What is 10% of 150?

Circle the correct answer.

 10 15 30 150

1 mark

2 Fill in the boxes to complete the sentence.

10% of 450 is [ ] , so 20% of 450 is  [ ] .

2 marks

3 Draw lines to match the percentage to the correct value.

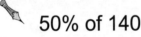

50% of 140	70
90% of 100	80
40% of 200	90

1 mark

4 Calculate:

30% of 100 = [ ] 50% of 220 = [ ]

2 marks

40% of 500 = [ ] 90% of 300 = [ ]

2 marks

5 Heidi has 50 pairs of shoes. She sells 20% of them.

How many pairs does she sell?

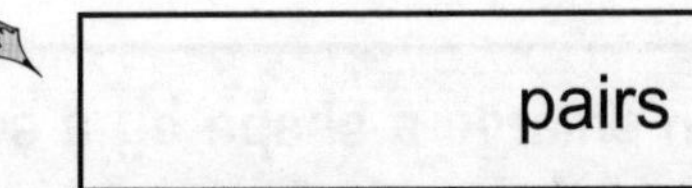

1 mark

Percentages of Amounts

6 Adam and his friends go to a restaurant for dinner.

The bill is £80. Adam pays for 25% of the bill.
How much does Adam pay?

£

1 mark

7 Calculate:

5% of 200 =

15% of 900 =

2 marks

8 Seb is making strawberries and cream for his family.

He uses 70% of a 250 ml pot of cream.
How many ml of cream does he use?

ml

1 mark

9 Frank has 30 mini doughnuts and eats 50% of them.
Lesley has 20 mini doughnuts and eats 70% of them.

Who eats more mini doughnuts?
Explain your answer.

2 marks

"I can find a percentage of an amount."

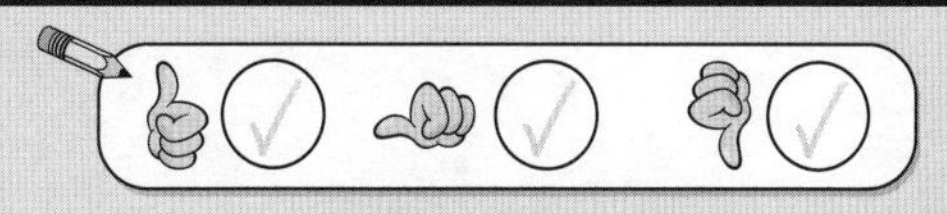

Comparing Using Percentages

1 Paula has 20 grapes.

She eats 10 of them. What percentage of the grapes has she eaten?

%

1 mark

2 Pippa is saving up for a bike which costs £50.

She has saved £30 so far.
What percentage has she saved?

%

1 mark

3 At the theatre, 60 out of 300 audience members buy an ice cream.

What percentage of the audience bought an ice cream?

%

1 mark

4 Bobby makes 25 sand castles at the beach.

The tide comes in and washes away 5 of them.
What percentage of the sand castles are **left**?

%

1 mark

Comparing Using Percentages

5 A clown has 50 balloons.

He gives away 30% of them.
How many balloons does he have left?

balloons

1 mark

6 Emika decorates some cupcakes. She puts stars on 40 of them, flowers on 25 of them and sprinkles on 35 of them.

What percentage of the cupcakes have stars?

%

1 mark

7 Circle the label that has the largest percentage discount.

Was £50
Now £5 off!

~~£25~~
Now £5 off

Was £200
Now £20 off

1 mark

8 Tamar scores 360 out of 400 points on her game.
Jacob scores 400 out of 500 points on his game.

Who scored the highest percentage of points on their game?
Explain your answer.

2 marks

"I can use percentages to compare amounts."

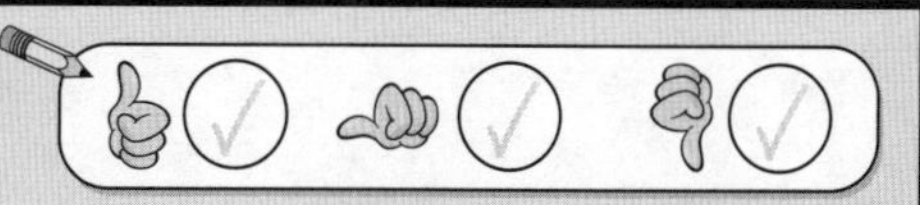

Unequal Sharing

1 In a bag of sweets, for every yellow jelly bean there are 3 red jelly beans.

There are 5 yellow jelly beans. How many red jelly beans are there?

Y R R R

× 5 × 5

Y Y Y Y Y ?

[ ] red jelly beans

1 mark

2 Look at the diagram below.

Fill in the boxes to complete the sentences.

For every [ ] rabbits there are [ ] ducks.

1 mark

If there were 4 rabbits, there would be [ ] ducks.

1 mark

3 On a pizza, for every 3 pieces of pineapple there are 4 pieces of ham.

There are 12 pieces of pineapple. How many pieces of ham are there?

[ ] pieces

1 mark

Unequal Sharing

4 Alex and Aaron go on a walk.
For every red squirrel they see, they see 2 grey squirrels.

They see 9 squirrels altogether. How many grey squirrels do they see?

grey squirrels

1 mark

5 Jaydene is sharing blueberries with her brother.

For every 2 blueberries she gives her brother, she gives herself 3.
Her brother has 10 blueberries. How many blueberries does Jaydene have?

blueberries

1 mark

6 In the cast for a TV programme, there are 4 women for every 6 men.

There are 50 people in the cast. How many women and men are there?

women

men

2 marks

"I can work out how to share things unequally."

Sequences

1 The rule for the sequence below is "add 2".

Write down the next two terms in the sequence.

1 3 5 7

1 mark

2 The rule for the sequence below is "subtract 3".

Write down the next two terms in the sequence.

20 17 14 11  

1 mark

3 A number sequence goes 3, 7, 11, 15.

Fill in the box to describe the rule to get from one term to the next.

Add

1 mark

What is the next term in the sequence? 

1 mark

4 Write down the next term of the sequence.

2 7 12

1 mark

5 Write down the next term of the sequence.

25 19 13

1 mark

Sequences

6 Write down the rule to get from one term to the next for these sequences.

1 6 11 16 21 — 1 mark

10 17 24 31 38 — 1 mark

18 14 10 6 2 — 1 mark

7 Write down the missing terms in the sequences.

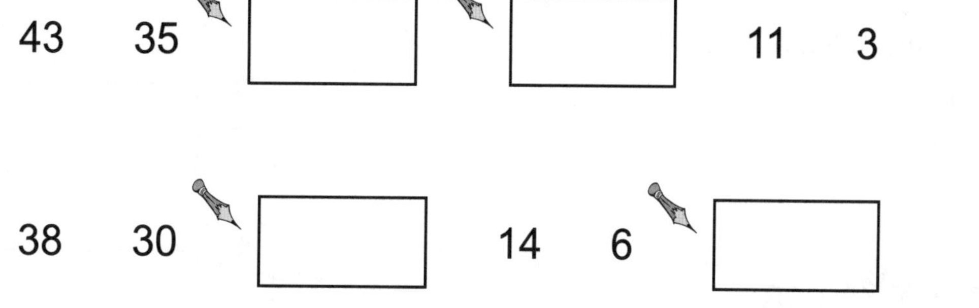

1 mark

1 mark

8 Fill in the missing numbers in this sequence.

1 mark

"I can generate and describe number sequences."

Missing Number Problems

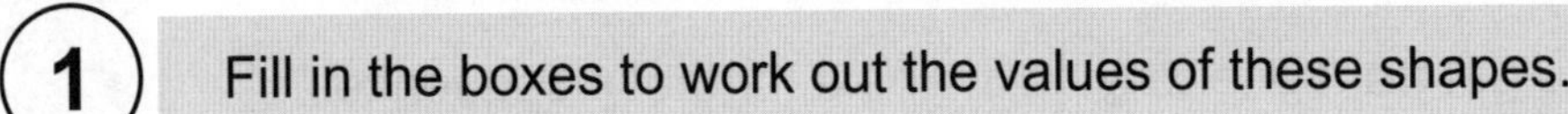

1 Fill in the boxes to work out the values of these shapes.

△ + 5 = 8 so △ = 8 − [ ] = [ ] 1 mark

◯ − 12 = 3 so ◯ = 3 + [ ] = [ ] 1 mark

2 ⬠ represents a number. Two lots of ⬠ equal 12.

What is the value of ⬠?

⬠ = [ ] 1 mark

3 The stars in the equations below represent numbers.

Find the value of each star.

☆ + 7 = 19 ☆ = [ ] 1 mark

3 × ✷ = 18 ✷ = [ ] 1 mark

4 Use these number machines to find the missing values.

10 → + 4 → ÷ 2 → [ ] 1 mark

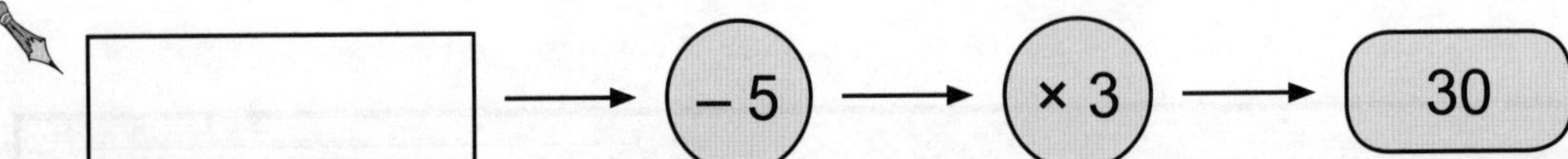

[ ] → − 5 → × 3 → 30 1 mark

Missing Number Problems

5 p represents a number. Start with p, multiply it by 5 and then add 3 to get 13.

Find the value of p.

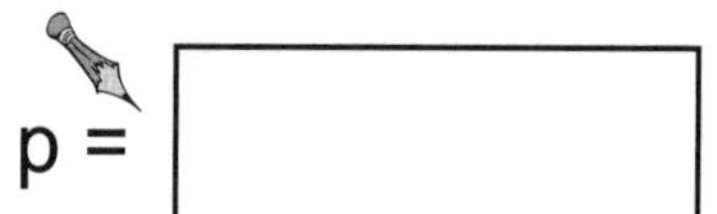

p =

1 mark

6 Alicja takes 56 photos. Devyn takes t photos. Alicja has takes seven times as many photos as Devyn.

Circle the equation that represents this.

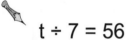

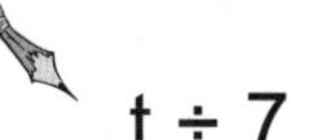

$t \div 7 = 56$ $7t = 56$ $t + 7 = 56$

1 mark

Work out the value of t.

t =

1 mark

7 Berta has grown y carrots. Jean has grown 2y carrots. In total, they have grown 30 carrots.

Circle the equation that represents this.

$y + 2y = 30$ $2y = y + 30$ $y + 2y + 30 = 1$

1 mark

What is the value of y?

y =

1 mark

"I can solve missing numbers problems using symbols and letters."

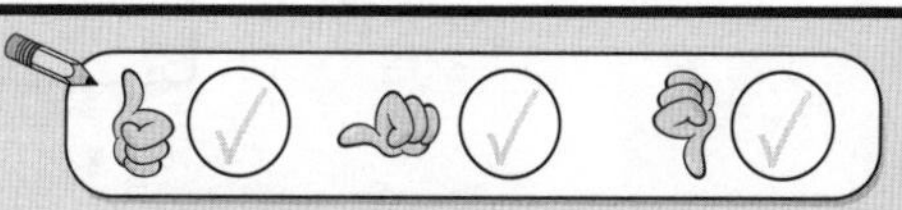

Two Missing Numbers

1 ○ = 5 and □ = 2

Circle the equation that is true.

○ + □ = 2 ○ + □ = 7 ○ + □ = 5

1 mark

2 Look at this equation: △ – ▽ = 2

Put a tick in the box next to **two** correct solutions.

△ = 10 , ▽ = 2 □ △ = 3 , ▽ = 1 □

△ = 5 , ▽ = 3 □ △ = 6 , ▽ = 3 □

1 mark

3 Pippin knows that a + b = 5. She is trying to guess the values of a and b.

If a = 1, what is the value of b?

b = □

1 mark

If b = 2, what is the value of a?

a = □

1 mark

4 Given that m + n = 10, write down any possible pair of values for m and n.

m = □ n = □

1 mark

Two Missing Numbers

5 Elspeth is thinking of two numbers, i and j.
She tells her friend that $i \times j = 20$ and that i is bigger than j.

List all the possible pairs of values for i and j.

1 mark

6 Look at this equation: $18 \div f = g$.
f and g are positive whole numbers and f is bigger than g.

Write down **all** the pairs of values of f and g.

2 marks

7 Dani makes her bed on D days each month. Edgar makes his bed on E days each month. Edgar makes his bed on 3 more days than Dani.

Circle the correct equation.

$E = 3D$ $D = E + 3$ $E = 3 + D$ $D = 3E$

1 mark

8 Estella is told that $R + 2S = 8$, where R and S are positive whole numbers.

Write down all the possible pairs of values for R and S.

2 marks

"I can find pairs of numbers to solve problems with two unknowns, and list all possible combinations."

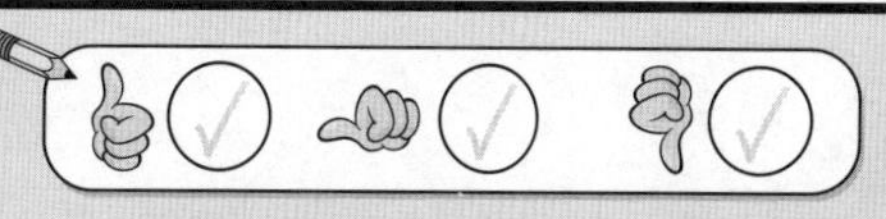

Formulas

1. The total number of stripes on all of Tamsin's jumpers is given by the formula: number of stripes = 10 × number of jumpers.

   Given that Tamsin has 5 jumpers, how many stripes are there?

   stripes

   1 mark

2. The formula for the number of blades on all the windmills on a hill is: number of blades = 4 × number of windmills.

   If there are 9 windmills on the hill, how many blades are there?

   blades

   1 mark

3. A music website charges the following fees each month: total cost = £50 + (£2 × number of albums downloaded).

   How much would you pay if you downloaded 12 albums?

   £

   1 mark

4. The number of diners that a restaurant can serve depends on the number of waiters working: diners = (waiters × 10) + 5.

   One evening, there are 7 waiters working in the restaurant. What is the number of diners that can be served?

   diners

   1 mark

Formulas

5 The length of a song contest, in minutes, is given by the formula:
length of the song contest = 60 + (3 × number of songs performed).

If there are 25 songs being performed, how long will the song contest last?

[ ] minutes

1 mark

6 A certain type of lorry has 12 wheels.

Fill in the box to write a formula for the number of wheels on any number of these lorries.

number of wheels = [ ]

1 mark

To calculate the number of spare mirrors they need, a lorry company halves the number of lorries they own and subtracts 5.
Use the symbols +, –, × or ÷ to complete this formula.

spare mirrors = number of lorries [ ] 2 [ ] 5

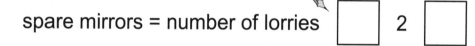

1 mark

7 A teacher tells her pupils that they should spend 2 hours revising for each of their tests, plus 1 extra hour.

Complete the formula.

time spent revising = [ ] + (number of tests × [ ])

How long should you spend revising if you have 5 tests?

[ ] hours

1 mark

"I can use formulas written in words."

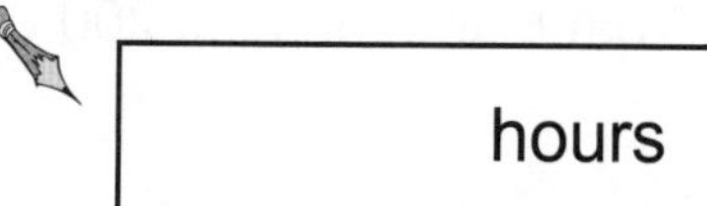

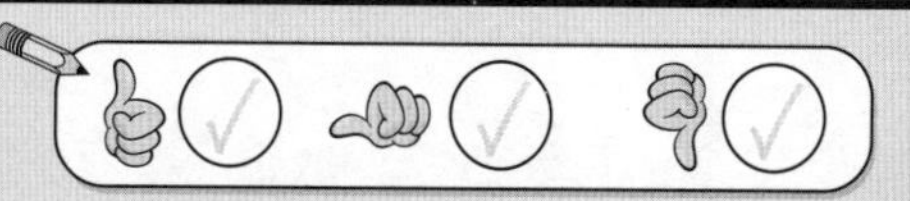

Units

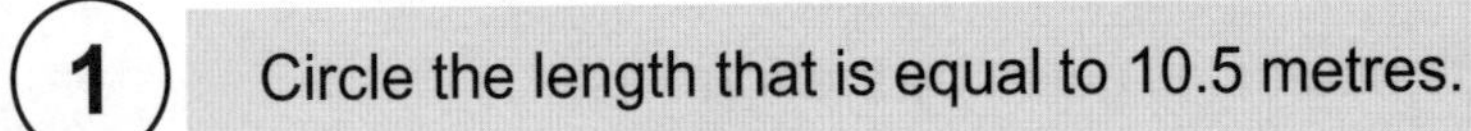

1 Circle the length that is equal to 10.5 metres.

105 cm   1050 cm   1500 cm   15 000 cm

1 mark

2 Complete the conversions below.

570 g = ______ kg   7.25 litres = ______ ml

2 marks

3 A builder has cut a plank of wood so that it is 8.52 m long.

How long is the plank of wood in cm?

cm

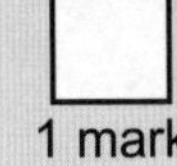
1 mark

How long is the plank of wood in mm?

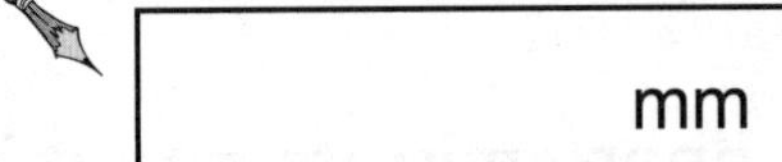
mm

1 mark

4 Flora has a bottle containing 0.35 litres of milk.
She pours 120 ml of milk on to her cereal.

How much milk is left in the bottle? Give your answer in ml.

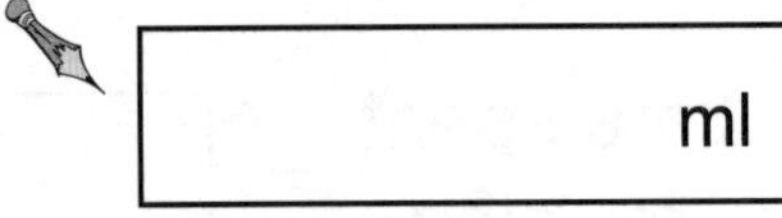
ml

1 mark

5 A doughnut has a mass of 32 g.

What is the mass of 200 doughnuts? Give your answer in kg.

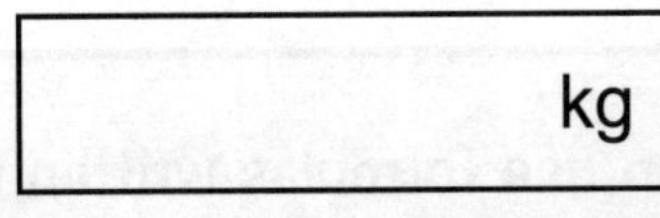
kg

1 mark

Units

6 5 miles is approximately equal to 8 km.

Convert the distances below by completing the calculations.

10 miles ≈ (10 ÷ 5) × 8 = [____] km — 1 mark

50 miles ≈ (50 ÷ [____]) × [____] = [____] km — 1 mark

64 km ≈ (64 ÷ [____]) × [____] = [____] miles — 1 mark

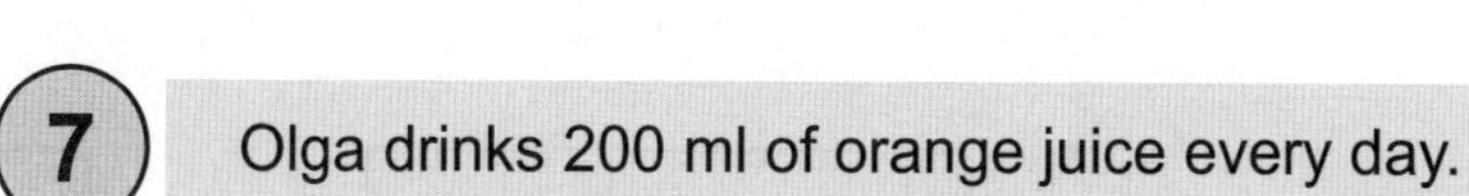

7 Olga drinks 200 ml of orange juice every day.

How many days will it take her to drink a 3 litre carton of orange juice?

[____] days — 1 mark

8 Ferdinand feeds his rabbit 25 g of food pellets every day.

How many kilograms of food pellets will he feed his rabbit in 10 weeks?

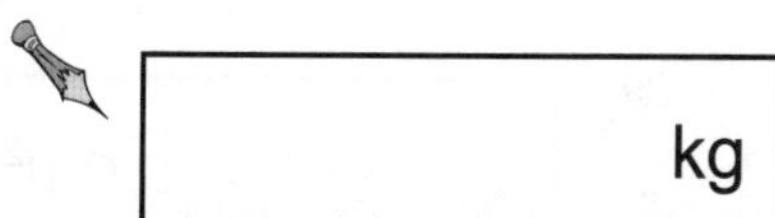

[____] kg — 2 marks

"I can convert between different units and solve problems involving unit conversions."

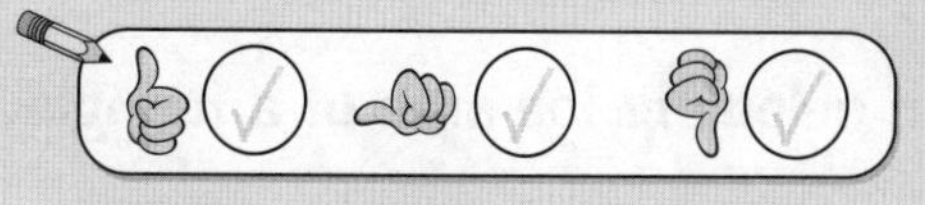

Area of a Triangle

1 A triangle is shown on the right.

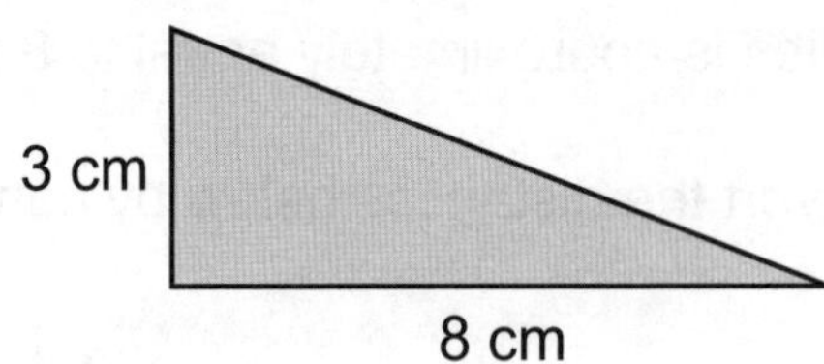

Complete this calculation to find the area of the triangle.

Area = $\frac{1}{2}$ × 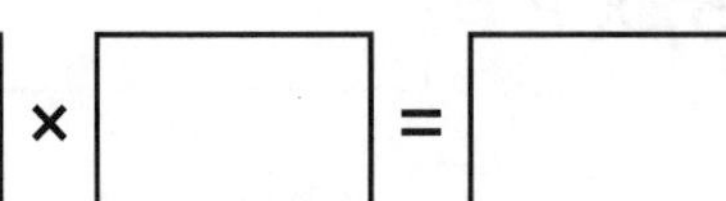 = cm²

1 mark

2 Calculate the areas of these triangles.

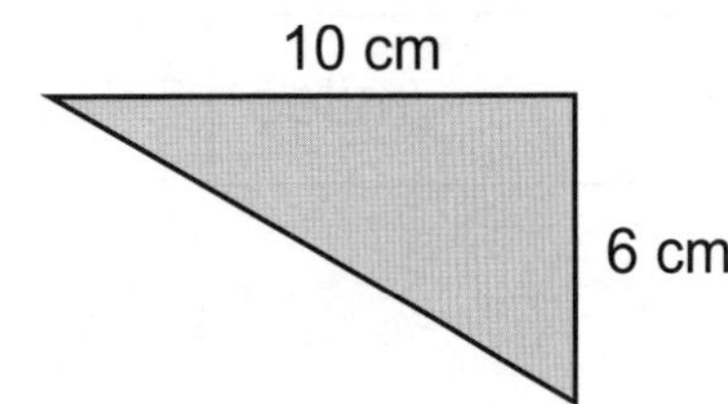

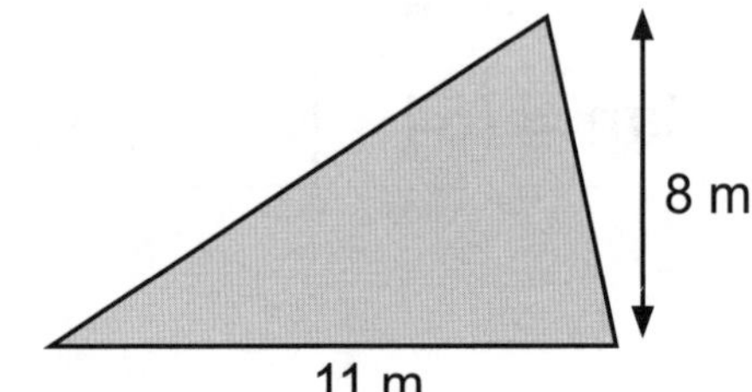

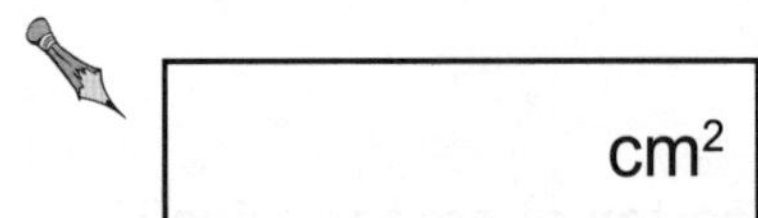

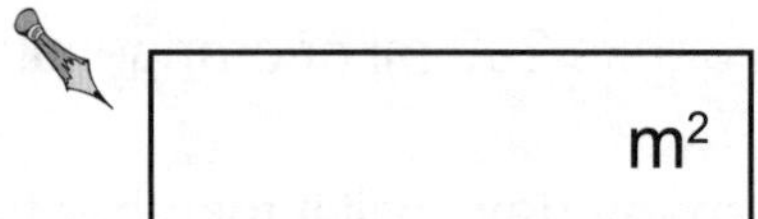

2 marks

3 Two triangles are shown on centimetre square grids below.

Use the formula for the area of a triangle to work out the shaded area of each grid.

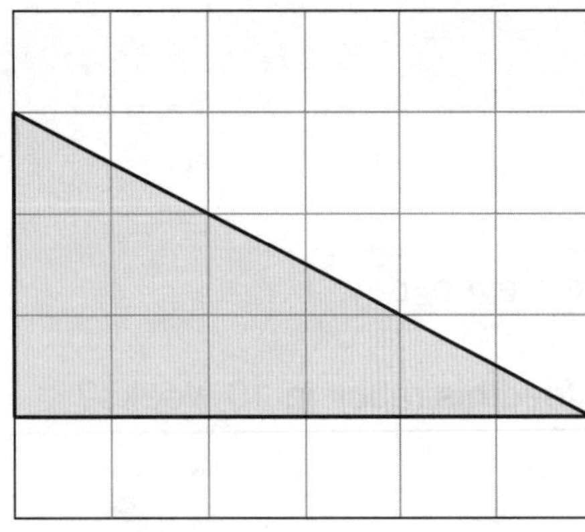

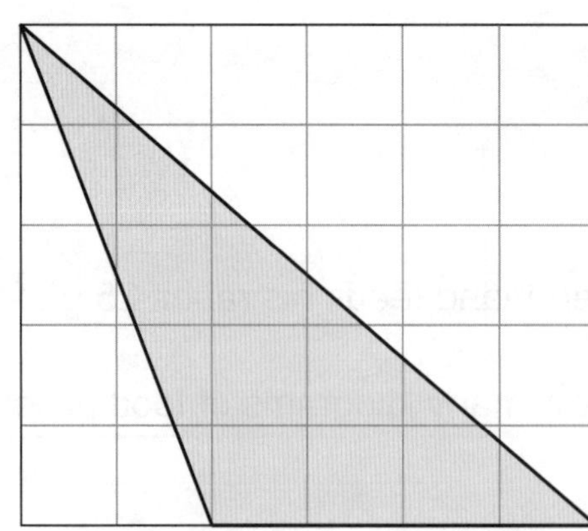

cm²

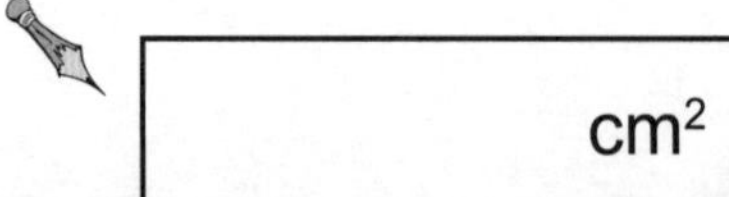

2 marks

"I can calculate the area of a triangle."

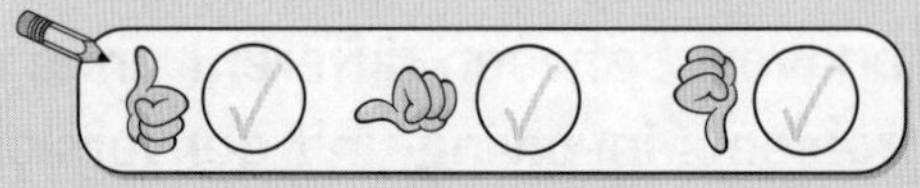

Area of a Parallelogram

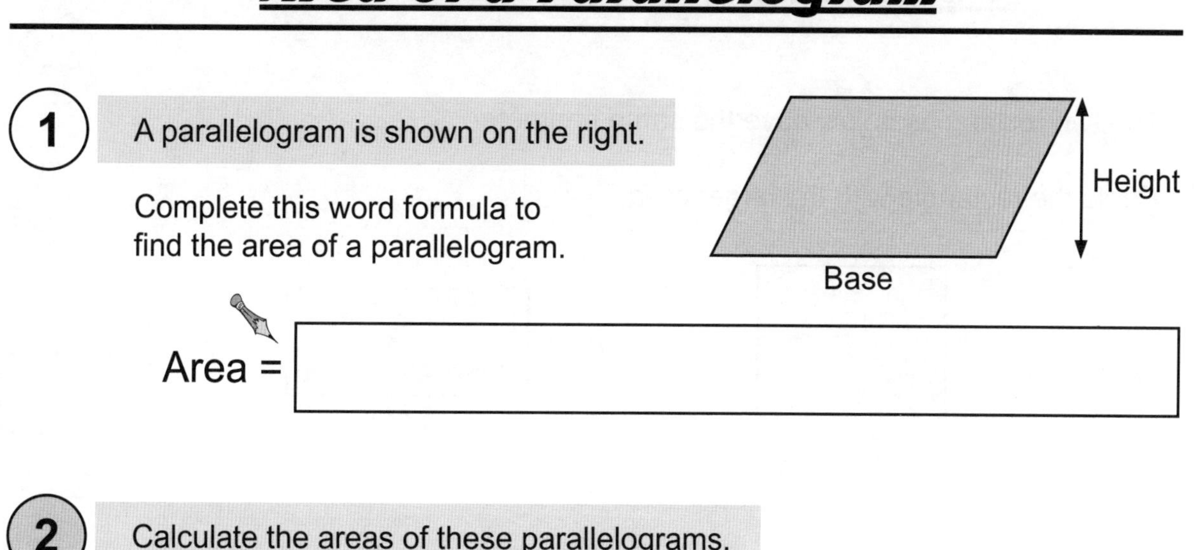

1 A parallelogram is shown on the right.

Complete this word formula to find the area of a parallelogram.

Area =

1 mark

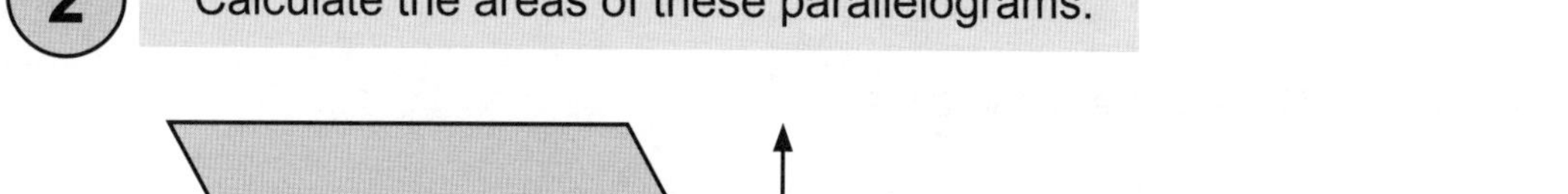

2 Calculate the areas of these parallelograms.

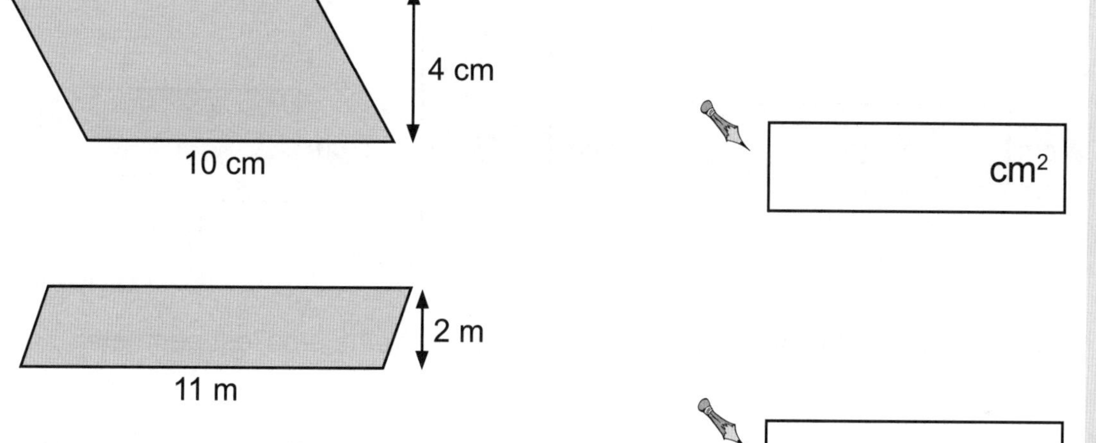

cm^2

1 mark

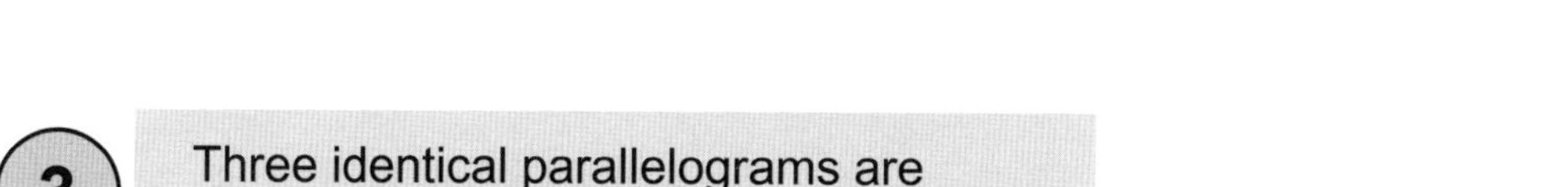

m^2

1 mark

3 Three identical parallelograms are joined together to create the logo below.

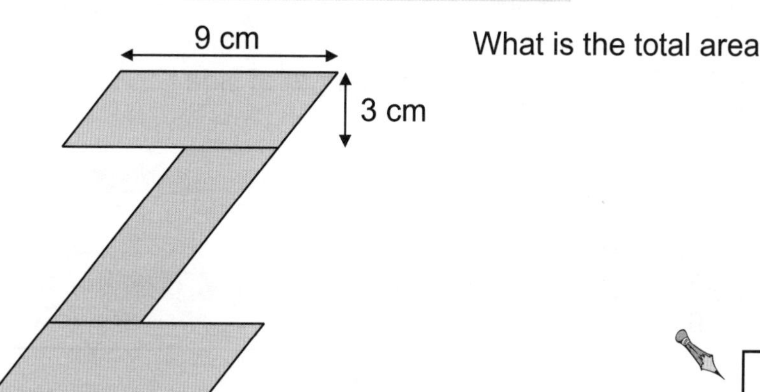

What is the total area of the logo?

cm^2

2 marks

"I can calculate the area of a parallelogram."

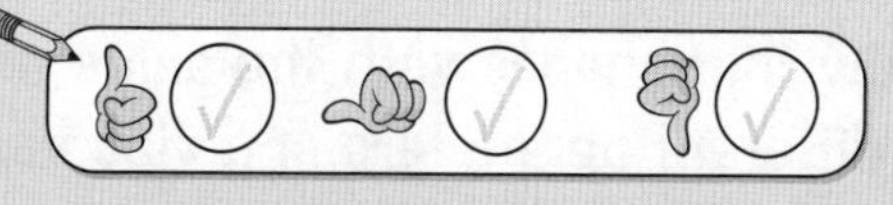

Perimeters and Areas

1 The two rectangles below have the same perimeter.

Circle the rectangle with the larger area.

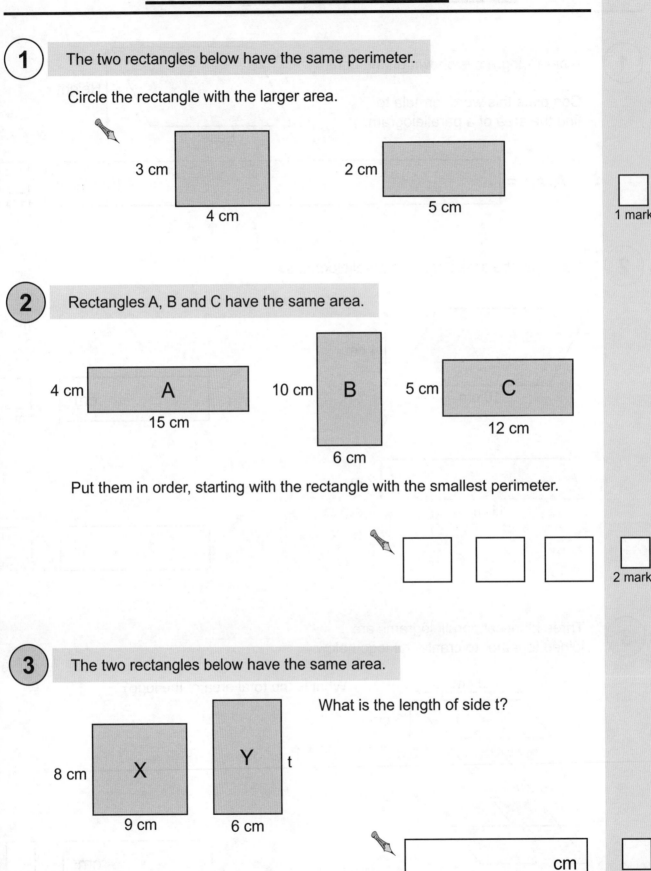

3 cm, 4 cm

2 cm, 5 cm

1 mark

2 Rectangles A, B and C have the same area.

A: 4 cm, 15 cm

B: 10 cm, 6 cm

C: 5 cm, 12 cm

Put them in order, starting with the rectangle with the smallest perimeter.

☐ ☐ ☐

2 marks

3 The two rectangles below have the same area.

X: 8 cm, 9 cm

Y: t, 6 cm

What is the length of side t?

cm

2 marks

"I know that shapes with the same area can have different perimeters and vice versa."

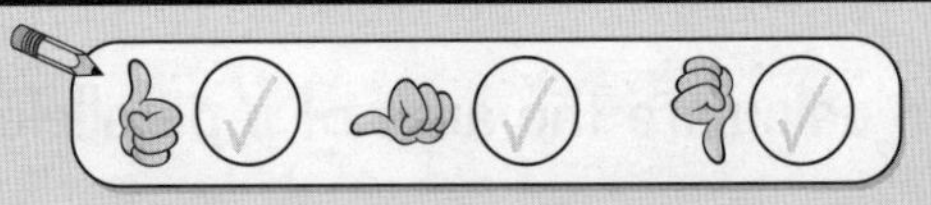

Volumes of Cubes and Cuboids

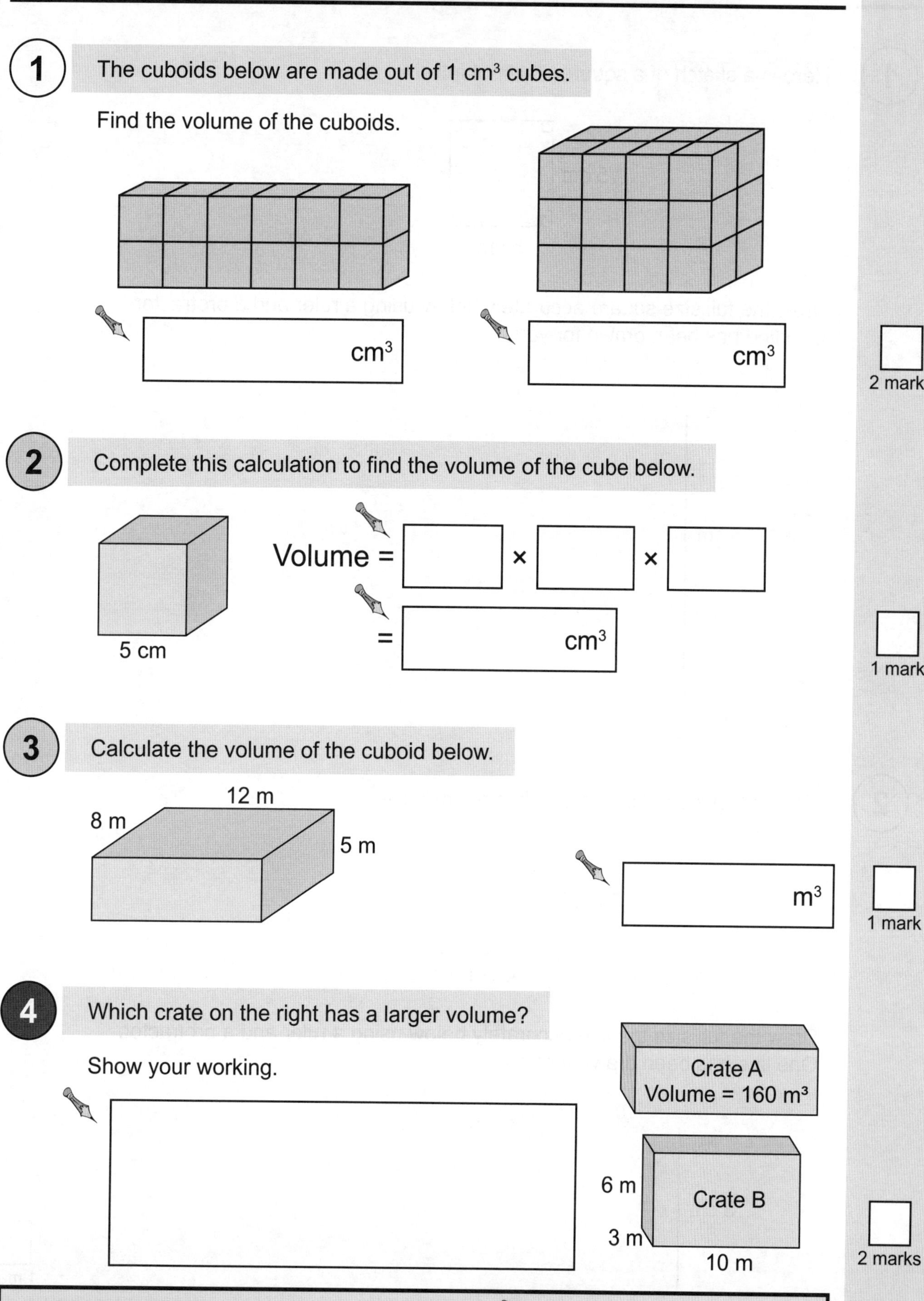

1
The cuboids below are made out of 1 cm³ cubes.
Find the volume of the cuboids.
cm³
cm³
2 marks
2
Complete this calculation to find the volume of the cube below.
5 cm
Volume = × ×
= cm³
1 mark
3
Calculate the volume of the cuboid below.
12 m
8 m
5 m
m³
1 mark
4
Which crate on the right has a larger volume?
Show your working.
Crate A
Volume = 160 m³
Crate B
6 m
3 m
10 m
2 marks

"I can calculate the volumes of cubes and cuboids."

Drawing 2D Shapes

Here is a sketch of a square. It is not full size.

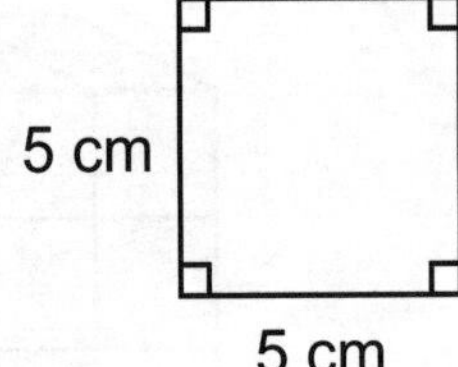

Draw the full size square accurately below using a ruler and a protractor.
One line has been drawn for you.

1 mark

2 Here is a sketch of a triangle. It is not full size.

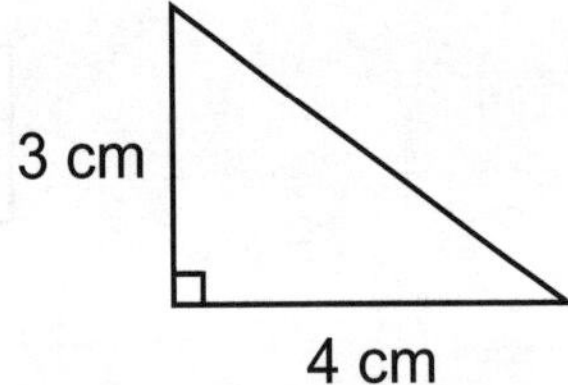

Draw the full size triangle accurately below using a ruler and a protractor.
One line has been drawn for you.

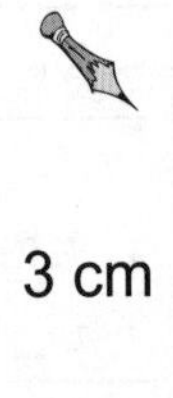

1 mark

Drawing 2D Shapes

Here is a sketch of a trapezium. It is not drawn to scale.

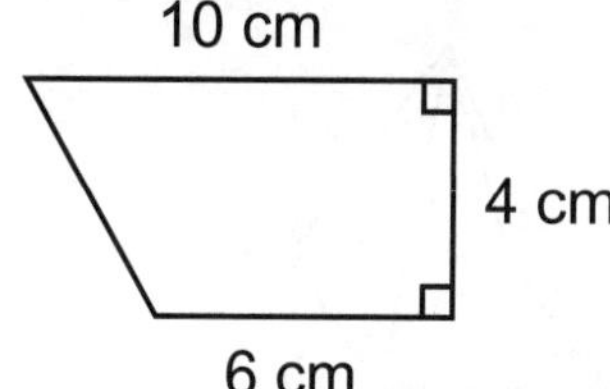

Draw the full size trapezium accurately below using a ruler and a protractor. One line has been drawn for you.

10 cm

1 mark

4 Draw a full size version of the sketch below accurately.

Use a ruler and a protractor.
One line has been drawn for you.

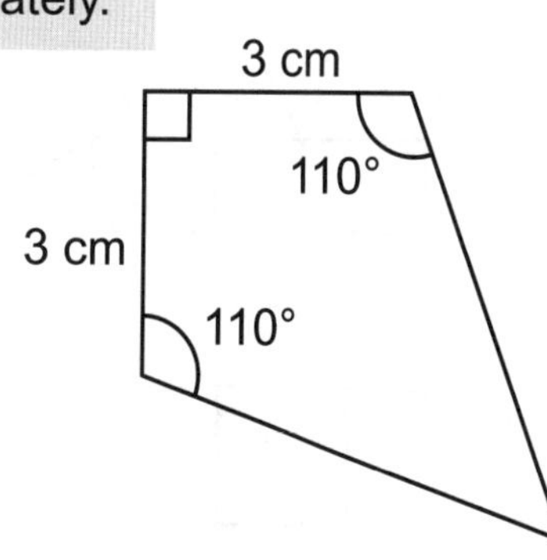

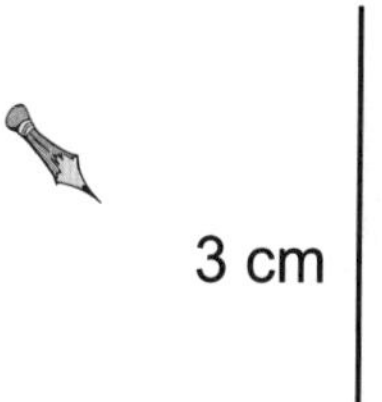

1 mark

"I can draw 2D shapes accurately."

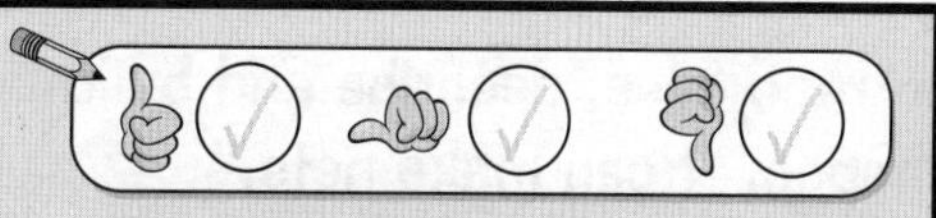

Making 3D Shapes

1 Write down the number of vertices each of these shapes has.

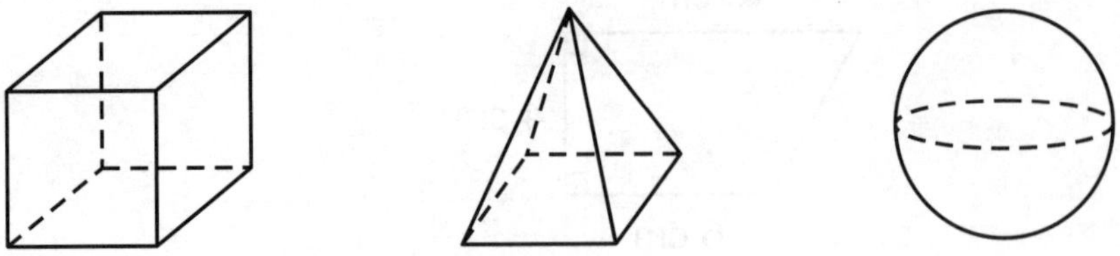

2 marks

2 Circle all the shapes that have fewer than 5 faces.

cuboid tetrahedron cone

triangular prism cylinder

2 marks

3 Which of these is the net of a triangular prism?

Put a tick below the correct answer.

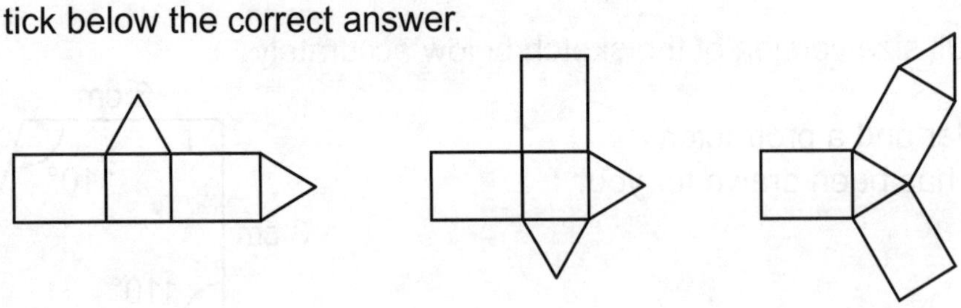

1 mark

4 What shape is this the net of?

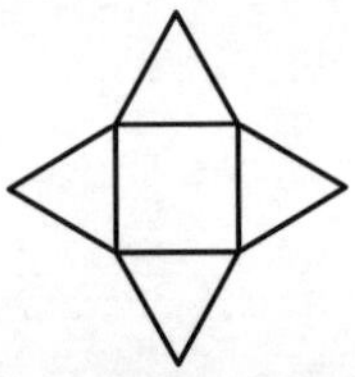

1 mark

"I can recognise, describe and build 3D shapes. I can make nets."

Making 3D Shapes

5 Draw an **accurate** net of this cube on the 1 cm square grid.

2 cm

1 mark

6 Draw a net of this cuboid on the grid below.

Two faces have been drawn for you.

1 mark

Draw the cuboid on the isometric grid. One face has been drawn for you.

1 mark

"I can draw nets of 3D shapes. I can use nets to draw 3D shapes accurately."

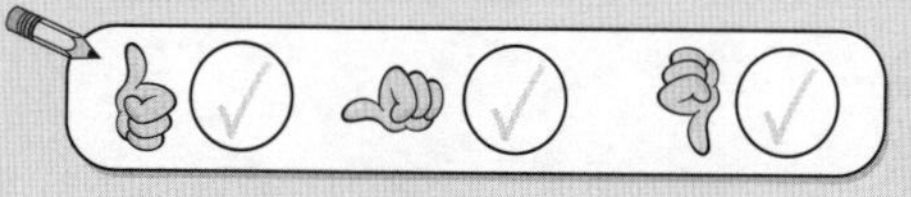

Shape Properties

1 Write these shapes in the correct parts of the table.

square | equilateral triangle | scalene triangle | parallelogram

	Not a quadrilateral	Quadrilateral
Sides are all equal lengths		
Sides are not all equal lengths		

2 marks

2 Which of these properties are true about a rhombus?

Tick **two** correct answers.

- ☐ Two pairs of parallel sides.
- ☐ Four acute angles.
- ☐ Diagonals cross at right angles.
- ☐ Four lines of symmetry.

2 marks

3 A kite has been drawn on the right.

Draw on any lines of symmetry.

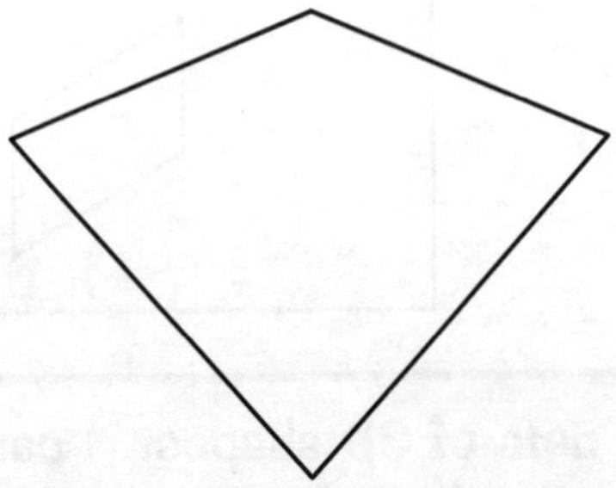

1 mark

Circle all the obtuse angles.

1 mark

Shape Properties

4 Complete the table to show the properties of some polygons.

Shape	Name	Number of lines of symmetry	Pairs of parallel sides
	regular hexagon		3
	equilateral triangle	3	
	rectangle		2
		8	4

2 marks

5 Draw lines to match each shape to its property.

isosceles triangle	all angles are obtuse
regular pentagon	only one pair of parallel sides
parallelogram	two pairs of equal sides
trapezium	always one line of symmetry

2 marks

"I know the properties of different shapes."

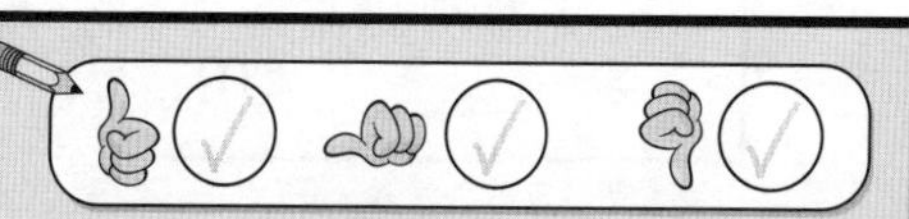

Circles

1 Draw a diameter on this circle using a ruler.

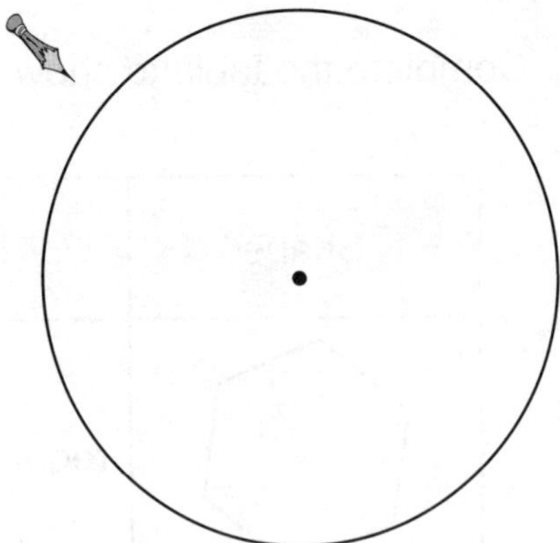

1 mark

2 Look at this circle.

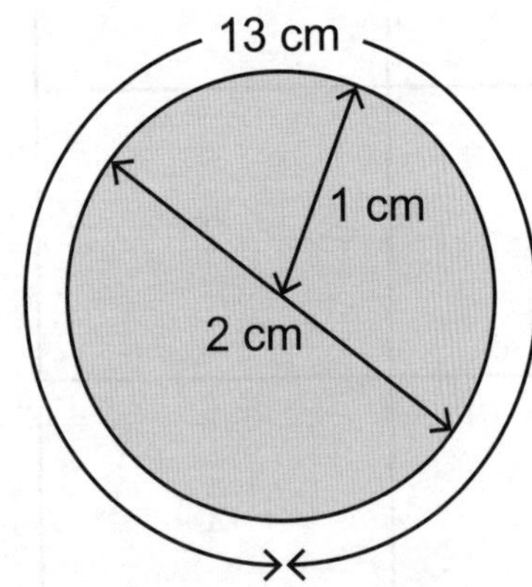

What is the circumference of the circle?

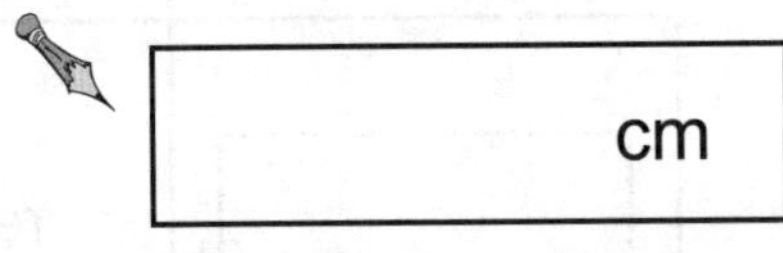

1 mark

What is the diameter of the circle?

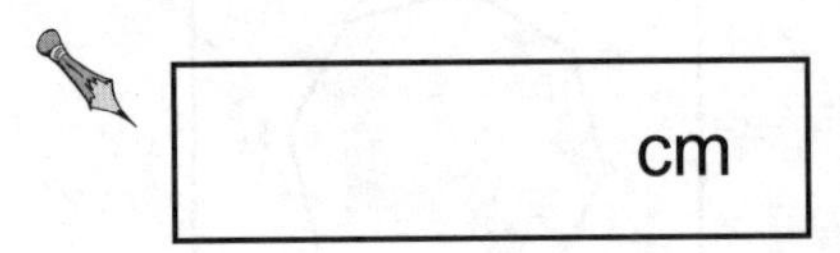

1 mark

3 Measure the radius of these circles using a ruler.

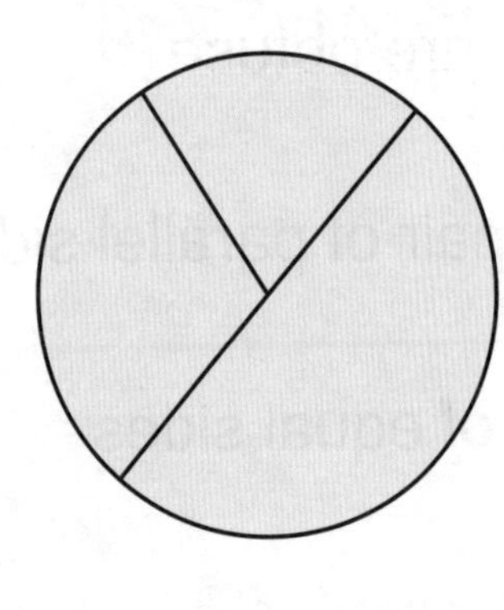

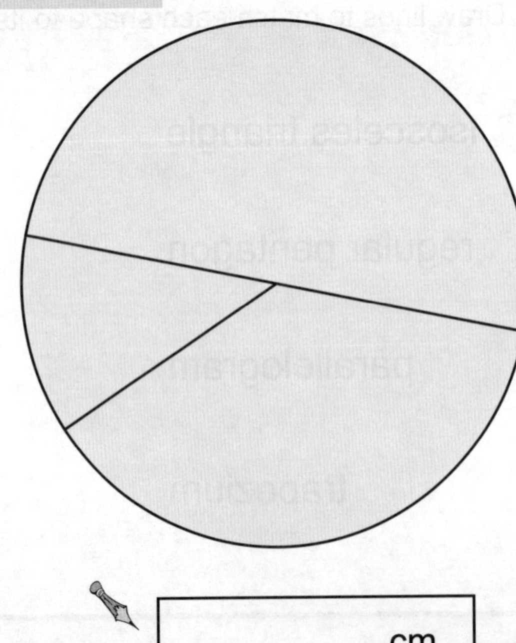

cm

cm

2 marks

Circles

4 The circle on the right is not drawn accurately.

What is the diameter of the circle?
Circle the correct answer.

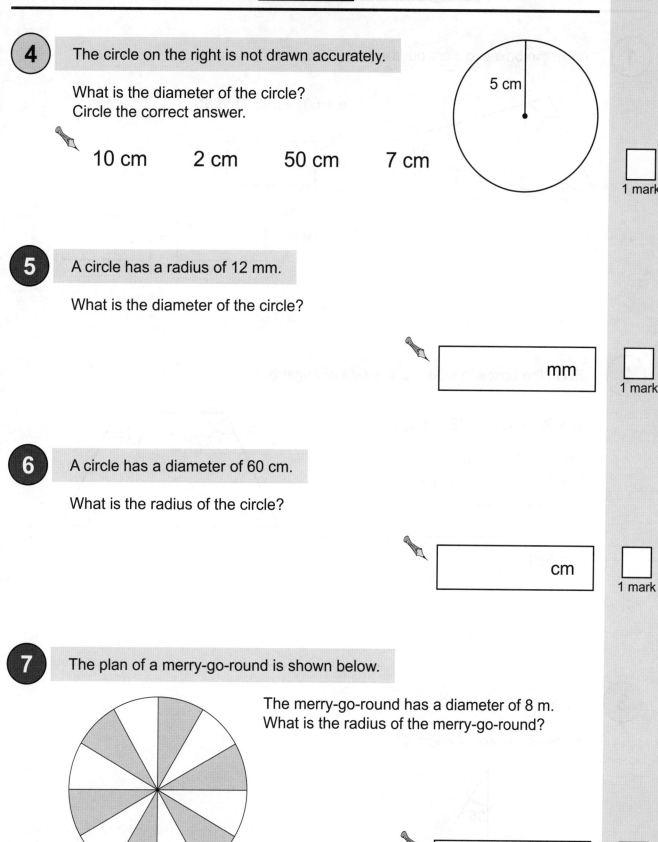

10 cm   2 cm   50 cm   7 cm

5 cm

1 mark

5 A circle has a radius of 12 mm.

What is the diameter of the circle?

mm

1 mark

6 A circle has a diameter of 60 cm.

What is the radius of the circle?

cm

1 mark

7 The plan of a merry-go-round is shown below.

The merry-go-round has a diameter of 8 m.
What is the radius of the merry-go-round?

m

1 mark

"I can name parts of a circle and I know that the diameter is twice the length of the radius."

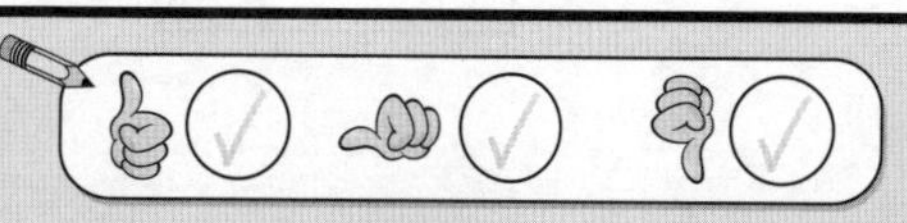

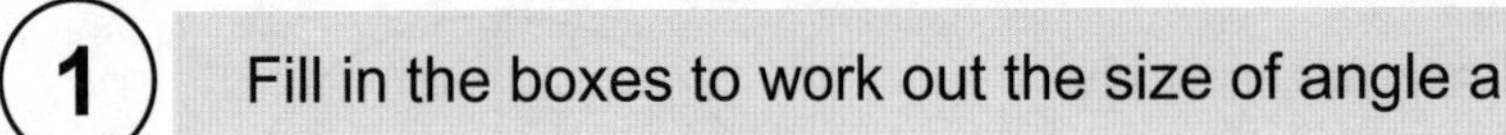

Angles in Shapes

1 Fill in the boxes to work out the size of angle a.

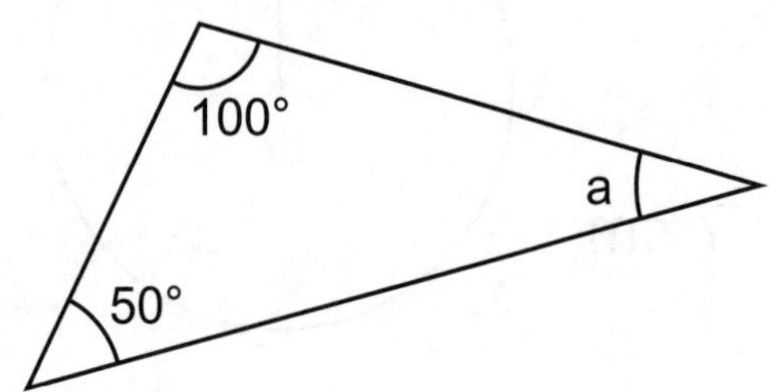

a + 50° + 100° = 180°

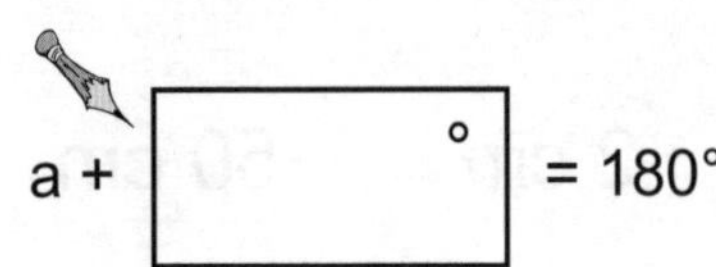

a + ☐° = 180°

a = 180° – ☐° = ☐°

1 mark

2 Fill in the boxes to work out the size of angle b.

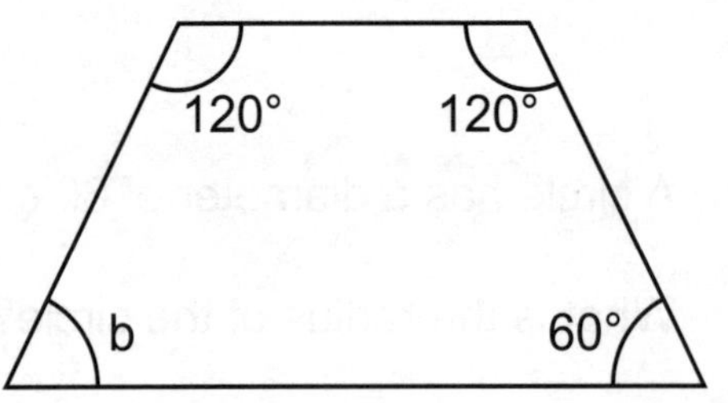

b + 60° + 120° + 120° = 360°

b + ☐° = 360°

b = 360° – ☐° = ☐°

1 mark

3 Look at the triangle below.

What is the size of angle c?

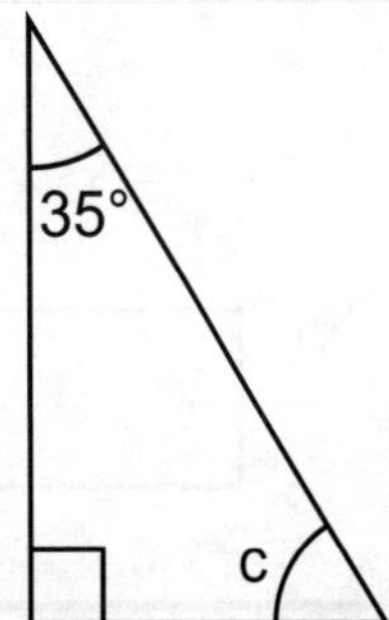

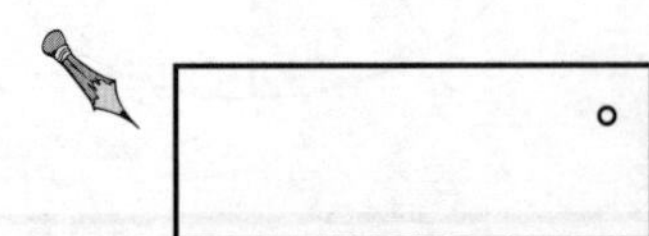

☐°

1 mark

Angles in Shapes

Look at the quadrilateral below.

What is the size of angle d?

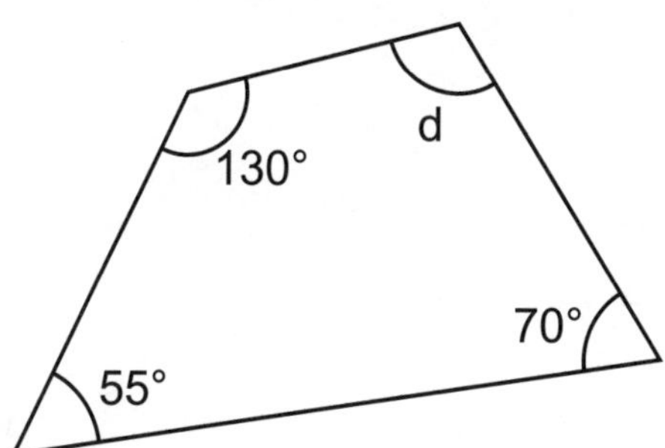

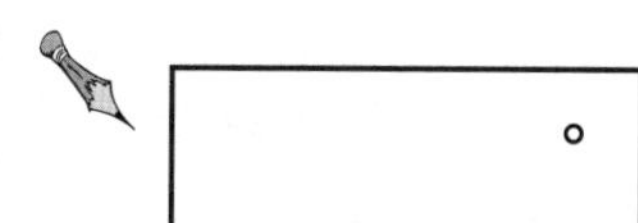

1 mark

5 The triangle below is isosceles.

Fill in the boxes to find the size of angles e and f.

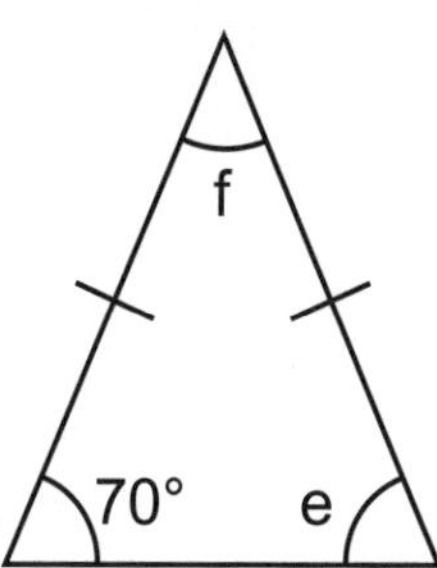

70° + e + f = 180°

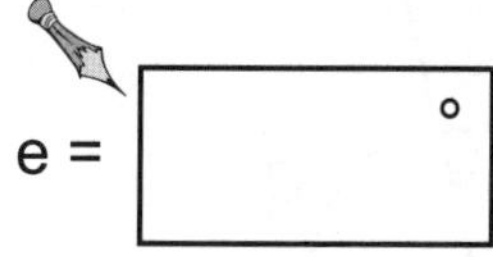

e = °

So f = 180° – ° = °

2 marks

6 Fill in the boxes to find the exterior angle and interior angle of this regular hexagon.

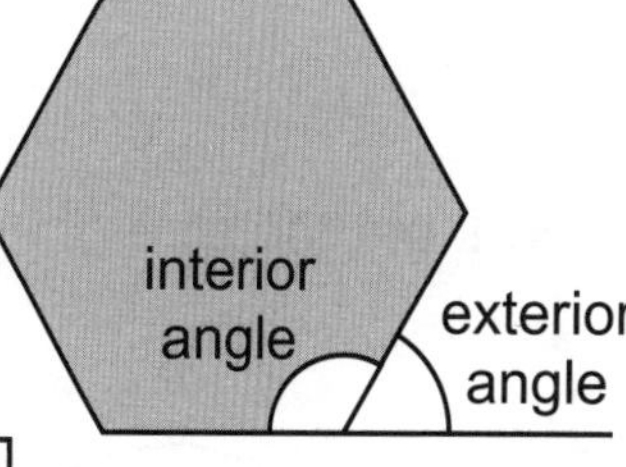

exterior angle = 360° ÷ number of sides

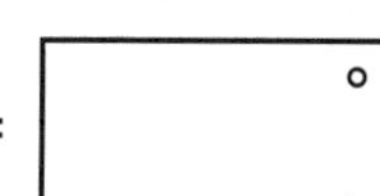

= 360° ÷ = °

1 mark

interior angle = 180° – exterior angle

= 180° – ° = °

1 mark

"I can use my knowledge of shapes to find missing angles."

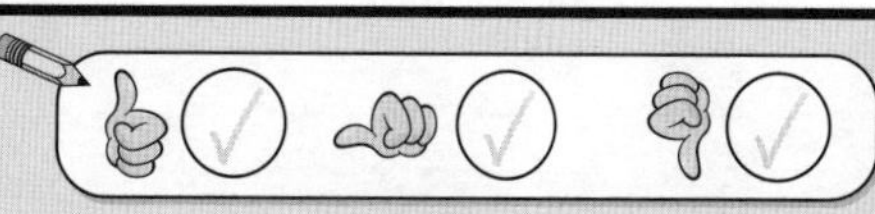

Angle Rules

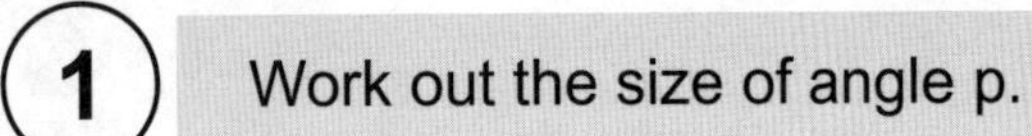

1 Work out the size of angle p.

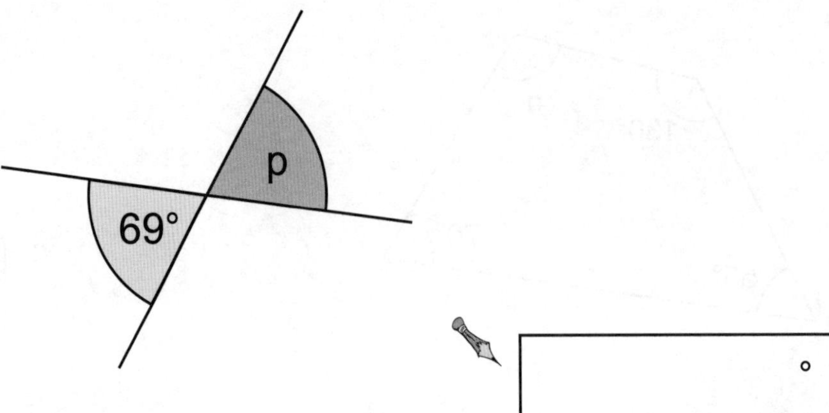

1 mark

2 Calculate the size of angle q.

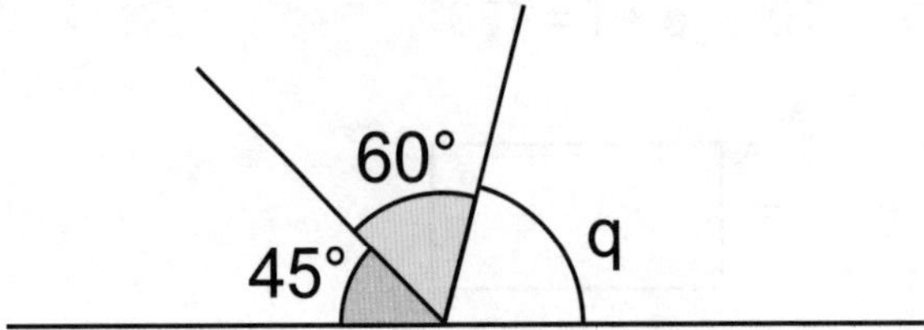

°

1 mark

3 Work out the size of angle r.

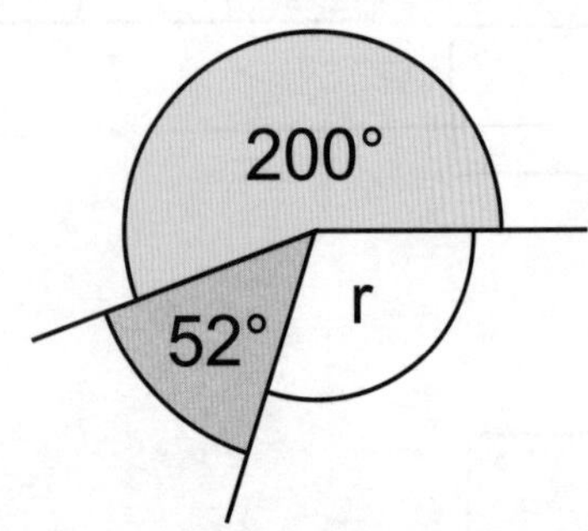

°

1 mark

Angle Rules

Calculate the size of angle s.

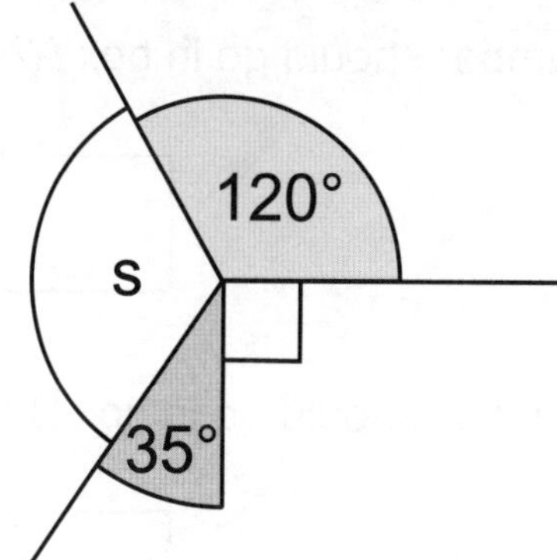

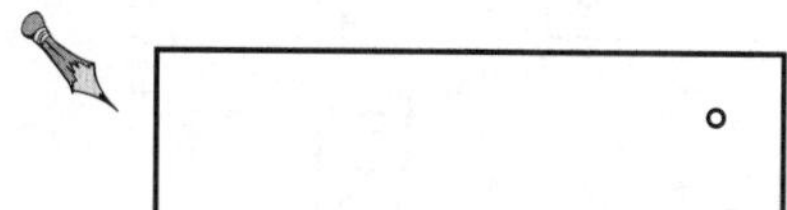

1 mark

5 Fill in the boxes to find the size of angles t and u.

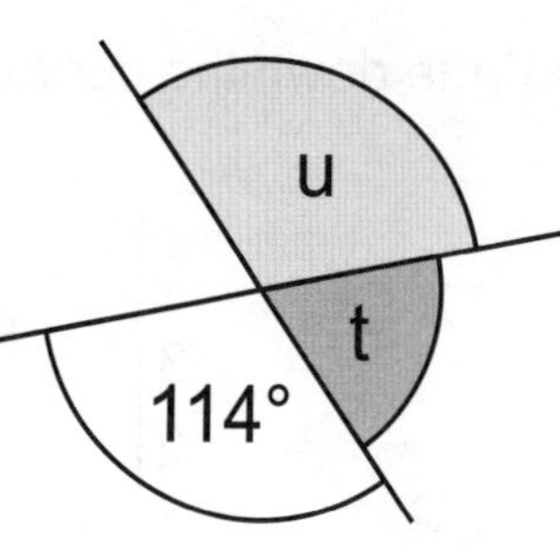

Angle ☐ is vertically opposite the 114° angle.

Angle ☐ is on a straight line with the 114° angle.

So angle t = ☐ ° and angle u = ☐ °.

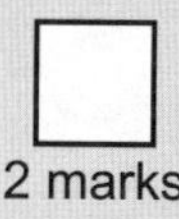

2 marks

6 Fill in the boxes to work out the size of angles v and w.

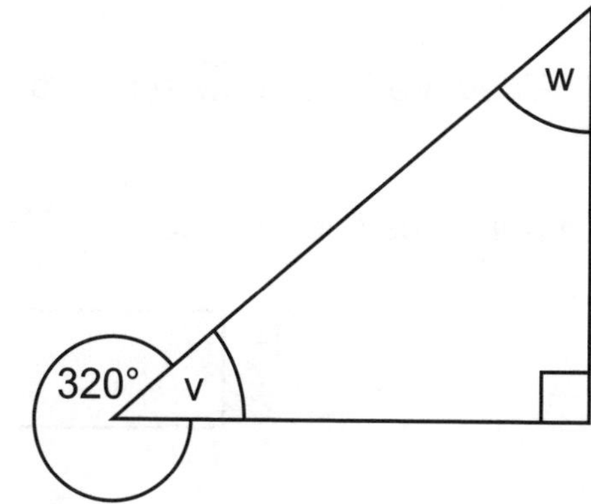

v + ☐ ° = 360°

So v = ☐ °

1 mark

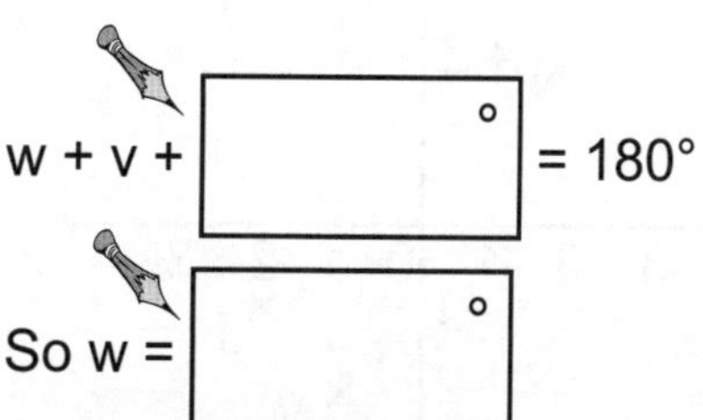

w + v + ☐ ° = 180°

So w = ☐ °

1 mark

"I can use rules to find missing angles."

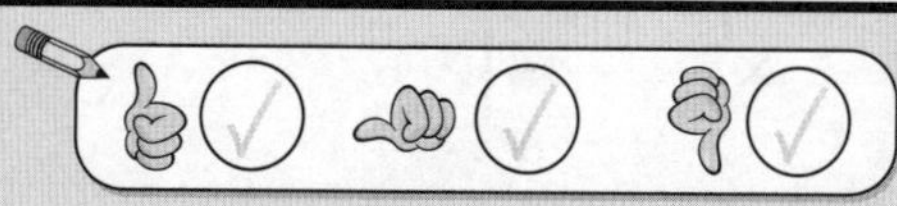

Coordinates

1 Some of the numbers are missing from the axes on this coordinate grid.

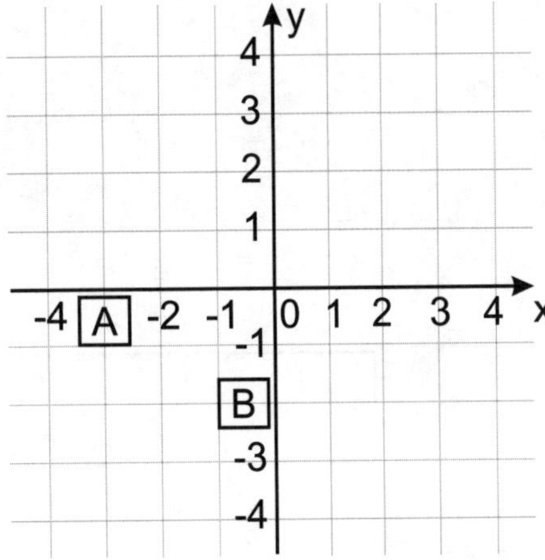

Which number should go in box A?

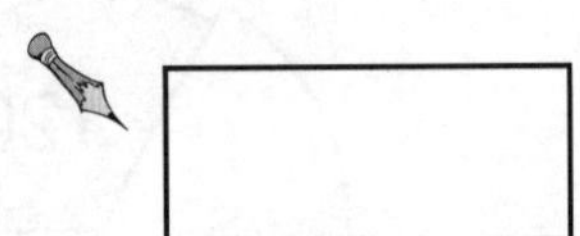

1 mark

Which number should go in box B?

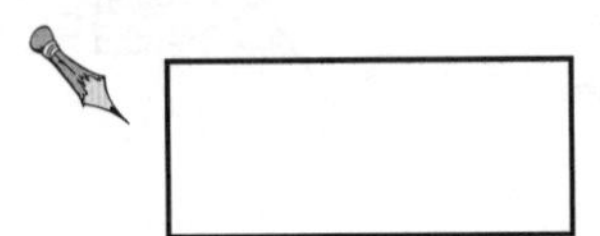

1 mark

2 Write down the coordinates of points P and Q.

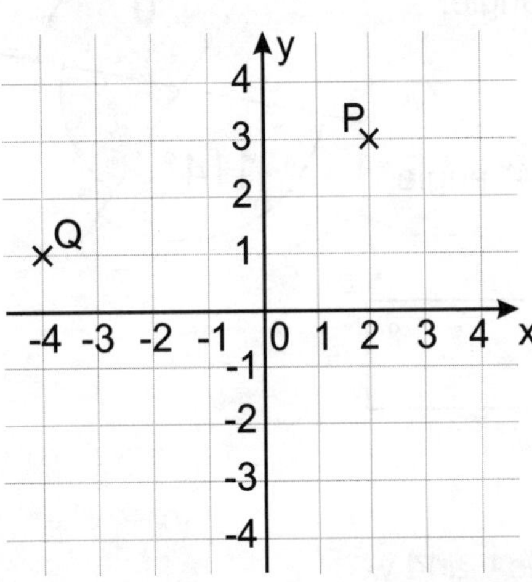

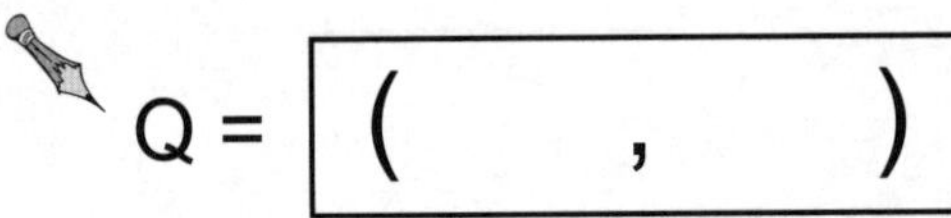

P = (,)

Q = (,)

2 marks

3 Some points have been plotted on this grid. They are labelled with letters.

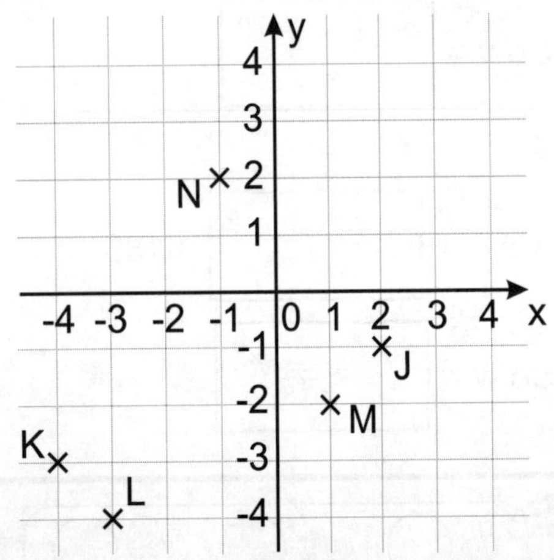

Which point has coordinates (–3, –4)?

1 mark

Which point has coordinates (2, –1)?

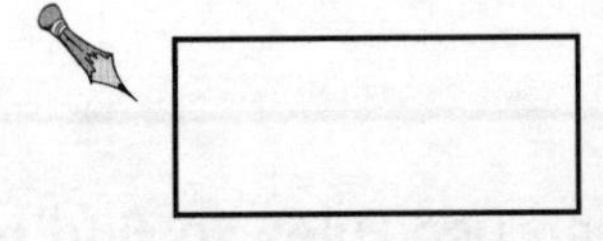

1 mark

Coordinates

4 Here is a coordinate grid.

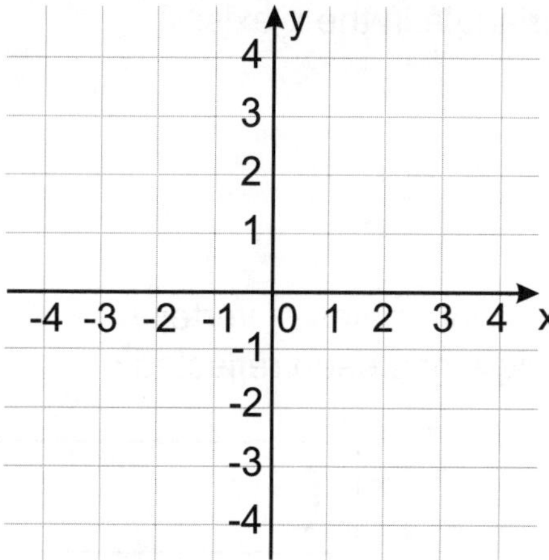

Put a cross at point (3, 2). Label it F.

1 mark

Put a cross at point (–4, 4). Label it G.

1 mark

5 A coordinate grid is given below.

Plot these four points on the grid:
(–4, –2), (–2, 2), (4, 2), (2, –2)

Join your points with straight lines to make a four-sided shape.

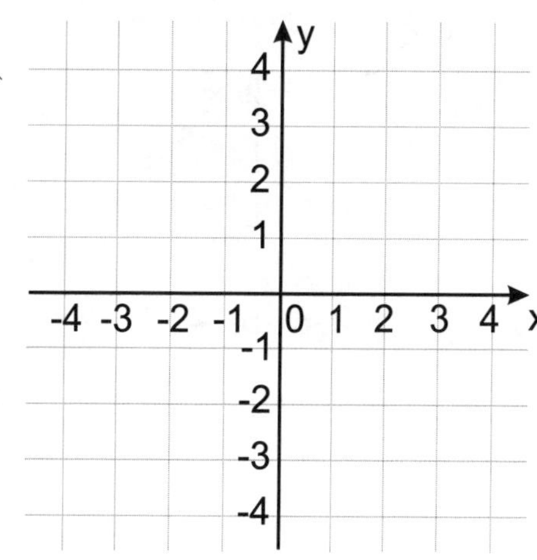

2 marks

What is the name of the shape you have drawn?

1 mark

6 Lexy has plotted three points on this grid.

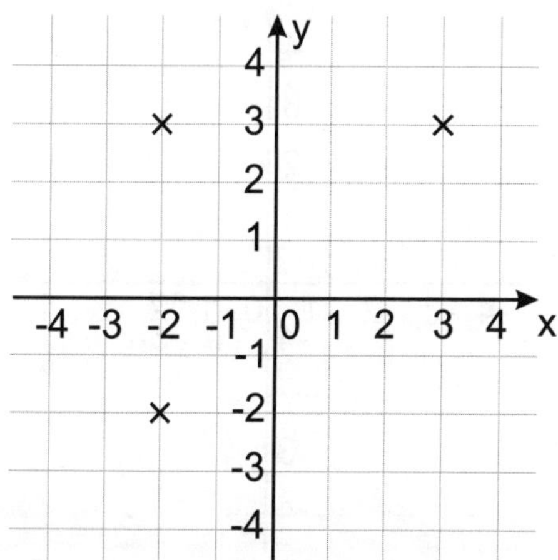

She wants to plot another point so the four points can be joined to make a square.

What point should Lexy plot?

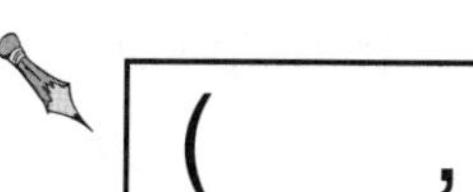
(,)

1 mark

"I can use coordinates in four quadrants."

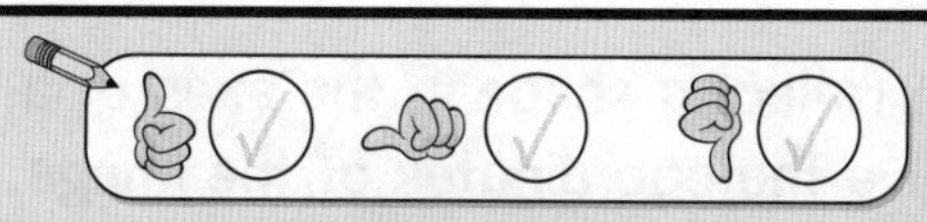

Reflection

1 A triangle has been drawn on the grid below.

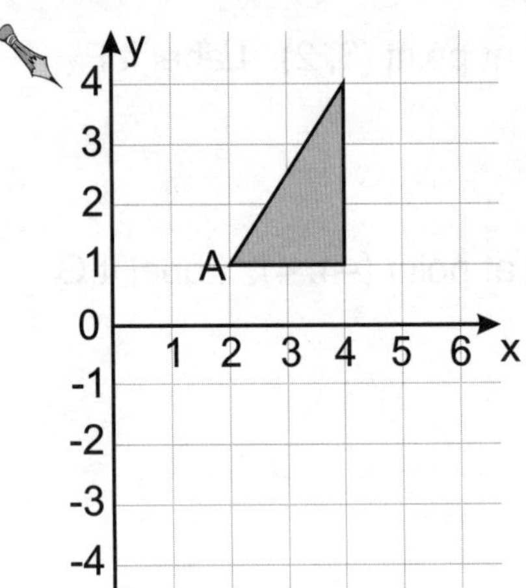

Reflect the triangle in the x-axis.

1 mark

What are the coordinates of vertex A after the triangle has been reflected?

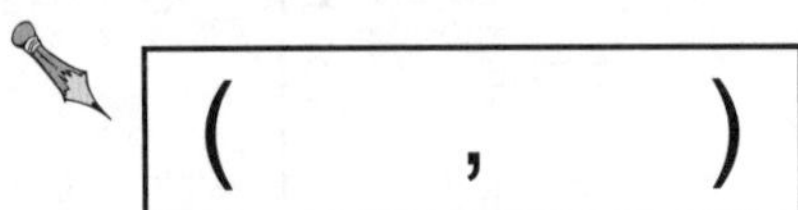

1 mark

2 Reflect the shape below in the y-axis.

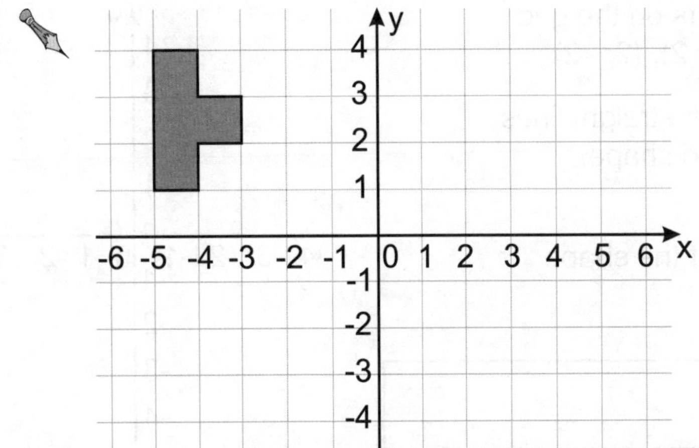

1 mark

3 A triangle has vertices P(–4, 1), Q(–3, 4) and R(–2, 1).

The triangle is reflected in the x-axis.

What are the coordinates of vertex Q after the triangle has been reflected? Use the grid to help you.

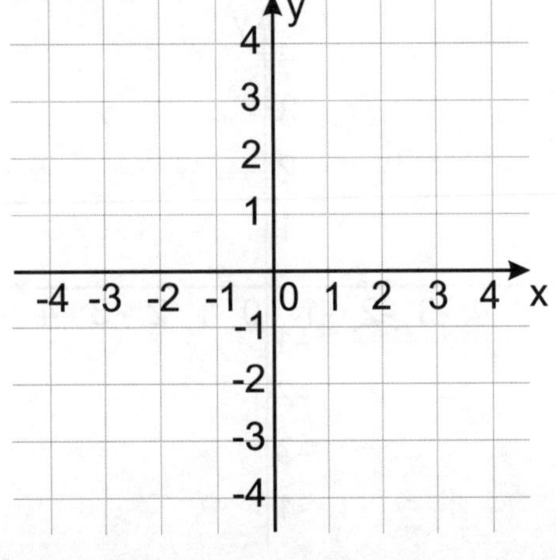

(,)

1 mark

"I can reflect a shape in the axes of a grid and give the coordinates of the image."

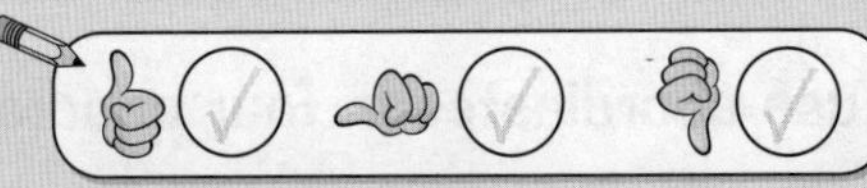

Translation

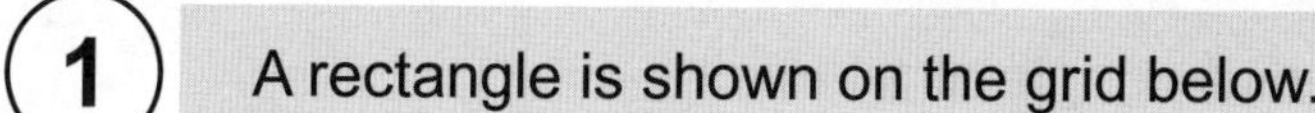

1 A rectangle is shown on the grid below.

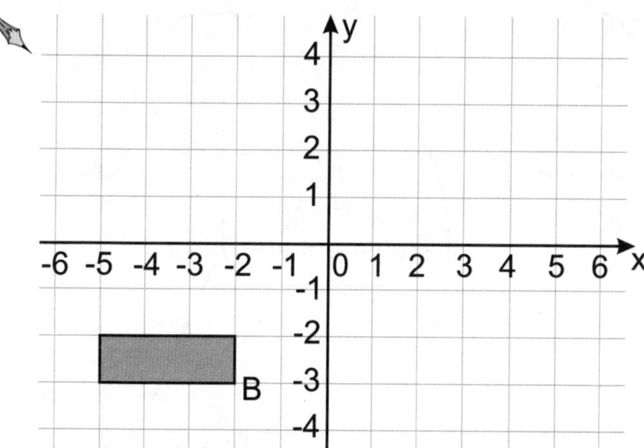

Translate this rectangle 6 units right and 4 units up.

1 mark

What are the coordinates of vertex B after the rectangle has been translated?

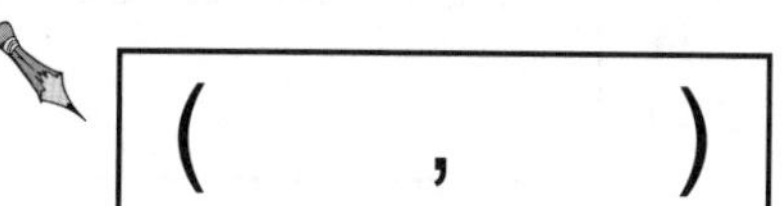

(,)

1 mark

2 Fill in the boxes to describe how to translate shape V to get shape W.

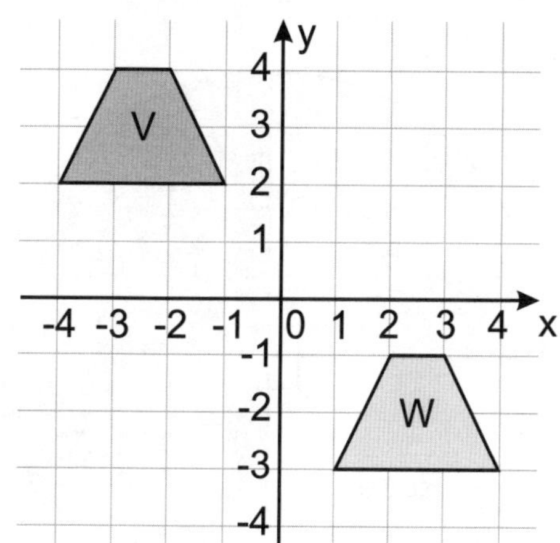

Move ☐ units ☐

and ☐ units ☐.

1 mark

3 A shape has a vertex P at coordinates (2, 2).

The shape is translated 4 units left and 5 units down.

What are the new coordinates of vertex P? Use the grid to help you.

(,)

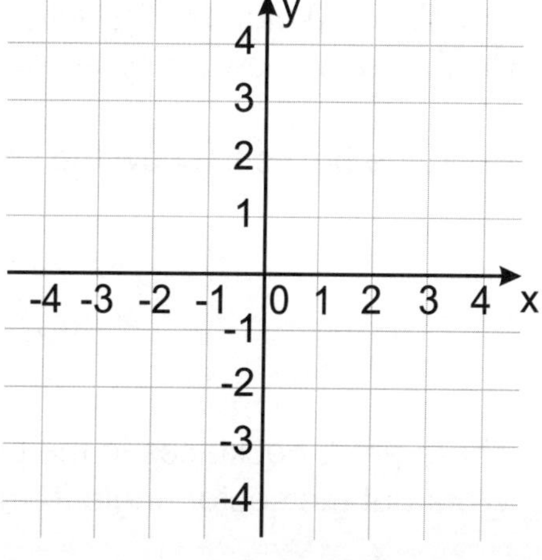

1 mark

"I can translate shapes using coordinates."

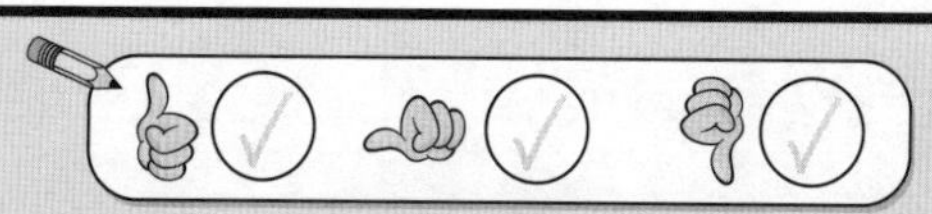

Pie Charts

1 The pie chart shows the favourite rides of people at a funfair.

Which ride was the most popular?

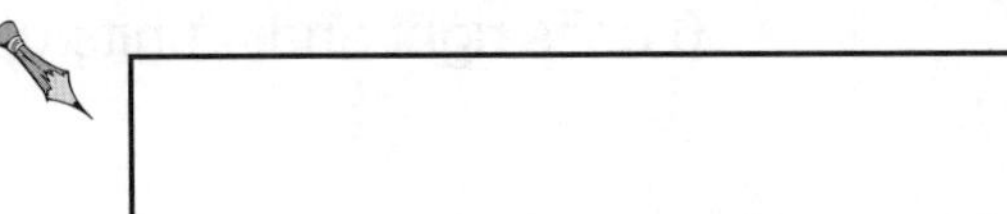

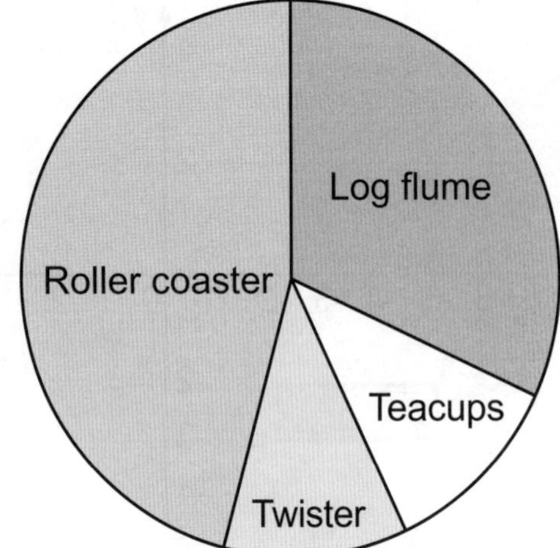

1 mark

Which ride was as popular as the teacups?

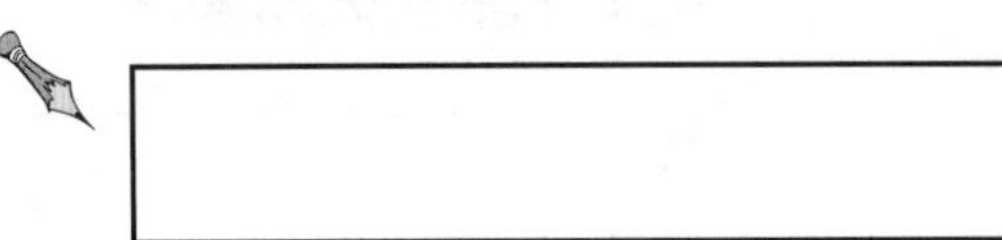

1 mark

2 Annika counts 20 flowers in her garden.

The pie chart shows the types of flowers.

How many tulips are there?

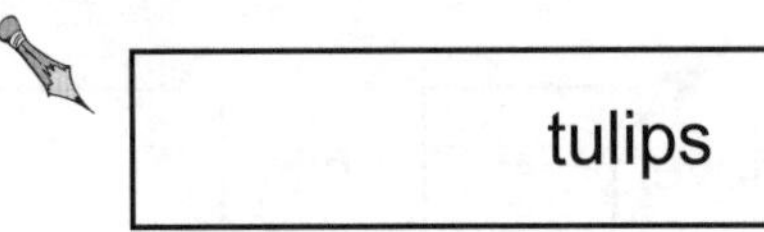

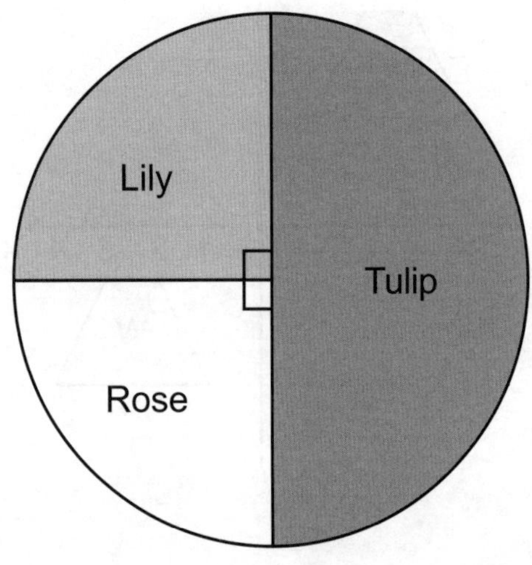

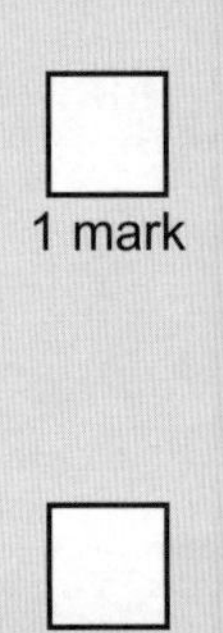

1 mark

How many lilies are there?

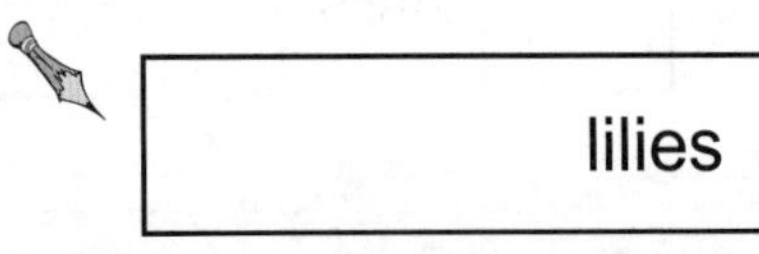

1 mark

3 Bret finds 10 pieces of jewellery in a box.
He wants to show the types of jewellery in a pie chart.

Fill in the boxes to show the sector angle for 1 piece of jewellery.

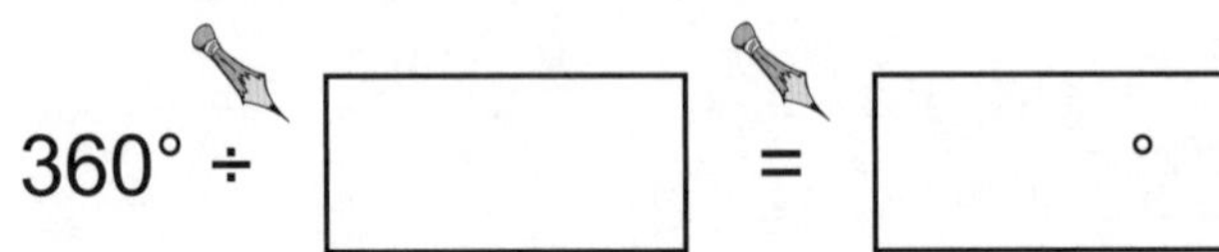

1 mark

There are 2 necklaces in the box.
Work out the sector angle for necklaces.

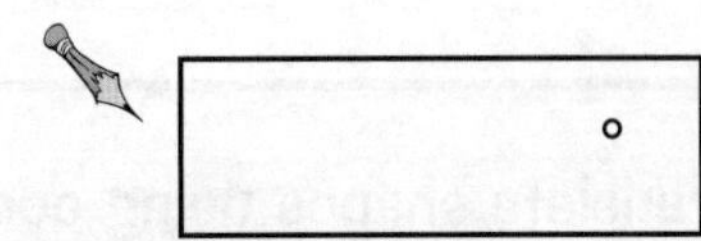

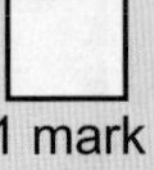

1 mark

Pie Charts

4 The table shows the favourite animals of 12 people.

Find the missing sector angles in the table, then draw a pie chart to represent this information.

Animal	Number of people	Sector angle
Horse	2	2 × 30 = 60°
Cat	4	
Dog	6	

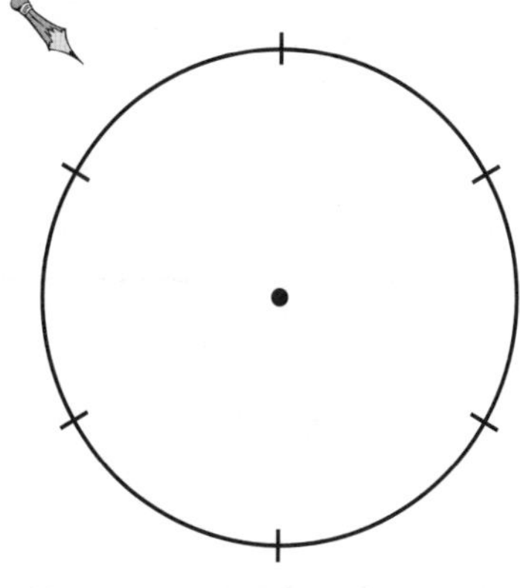

2 marks

5 30 people were asked, "Do you like bananas?"

The answers are shown in the pie chart.

What is the angle of the sector that represents 'Yes'?

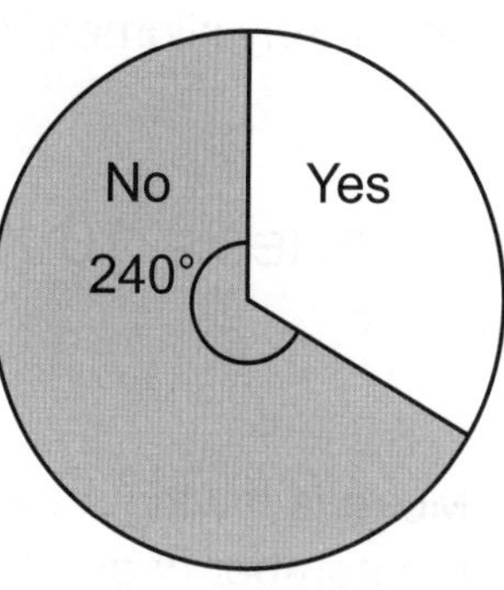

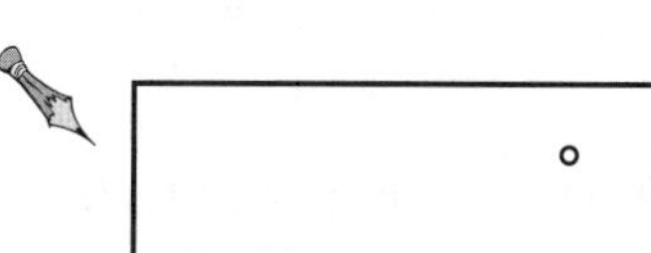

1 mark

How many people answered 'Yes'?

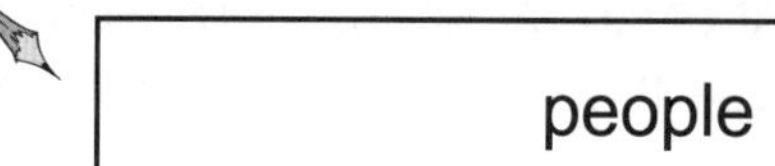

1 mark

6 60 clowns are at a circus.
Their hair colours are shown in the pie chart.

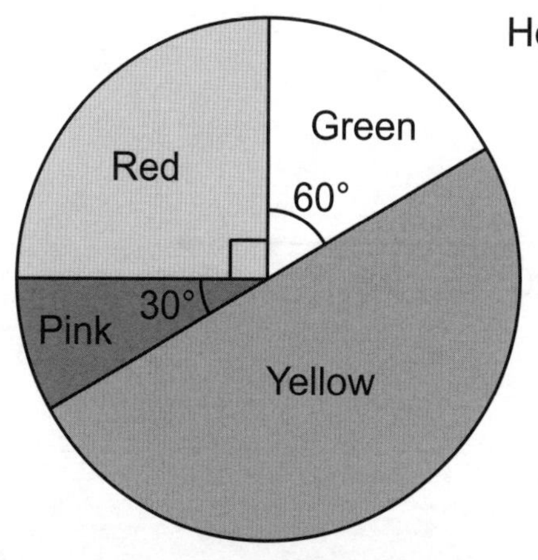

How many clowns have green or yellow hair?

clowns

1 mark

"I can understand, draw and interpret pie charts."

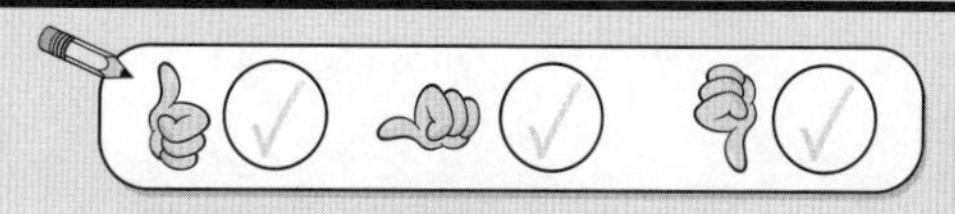

Line Graphs

1 The graph below shows how to convert between miles and kilometres.

Approximately how many kilometres are there in 5 miles?

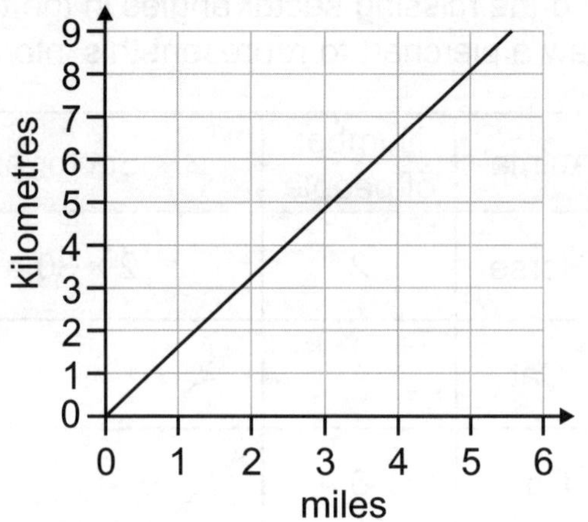

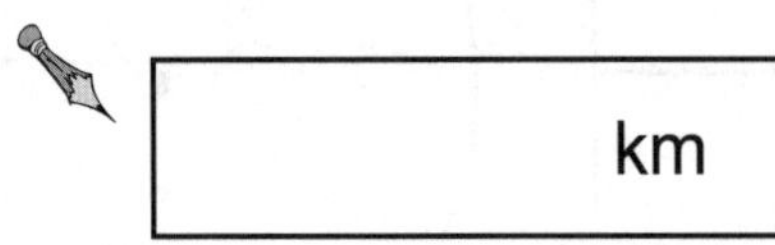

1 mark

Fill in the boxes to work out approximately how many kilometres there are in 50 miles.

50 miles = 10 × 5 miles ≈ 10 × [ ] km = [ ] km

1 mark

2 Moira is having a party. The line graph below shows the number of guests at the party in the first 25 minutes.

After 30 minutes, there were 14 guests at the party. Use this information to complete the line graph.

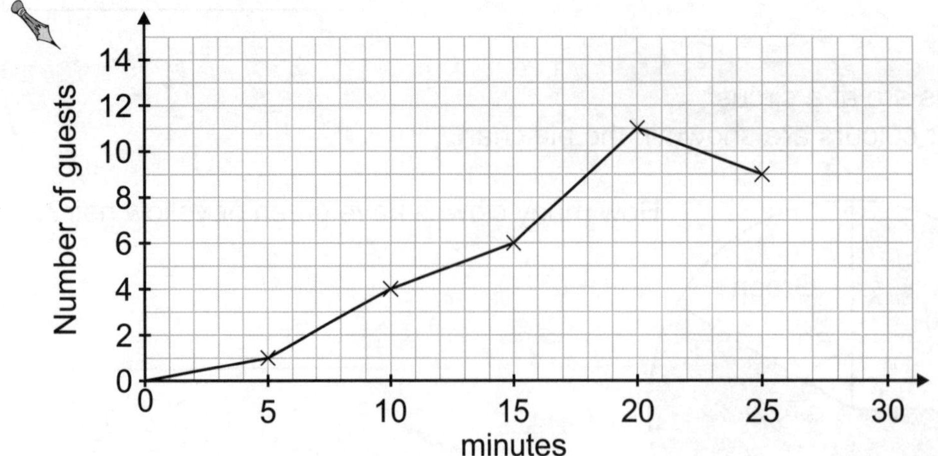

1 mark

How many more guests were at the party after 20 minutes than after 10 minutes?

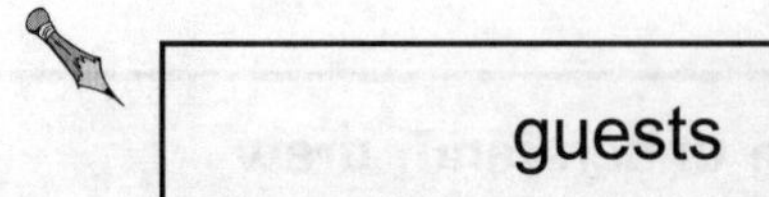

1 mark

Line Graphs

A captain records the speed of his ship as it sails away from the dock.

He writes his results in the table below.

Distance (km)	0	1	2	3	4	5
Speed (km/h)	0	15	25	30	30	40

Plot a line graph of the data in the table.

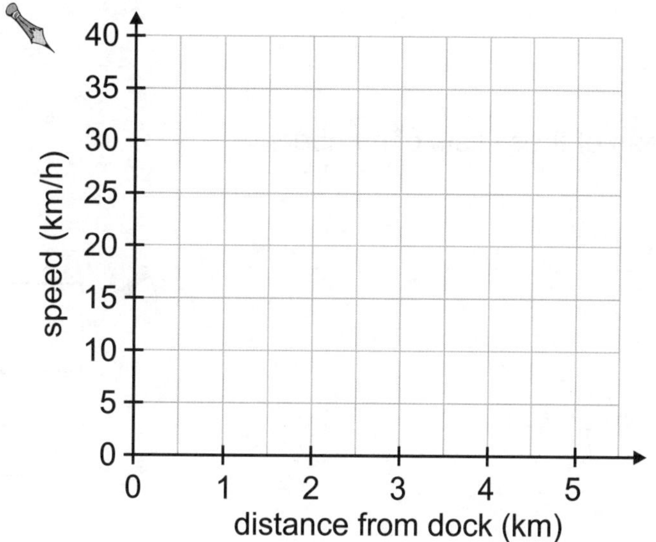

1 mark

How far was the ship from the dock when it first reached a speed of 30 km/h?

km

1 mark

What was the top speed that the ship reached?

km/h

1 mark

Part of this sentence is missing.

The biggest increase in speed was between ______ from the dock.

Which of these would complete the sentence?
Circle the correct answer.

0 and 1 km   1 and 2 km   2 and 3 km

1 mark

"I can interpret and construct line graphs."

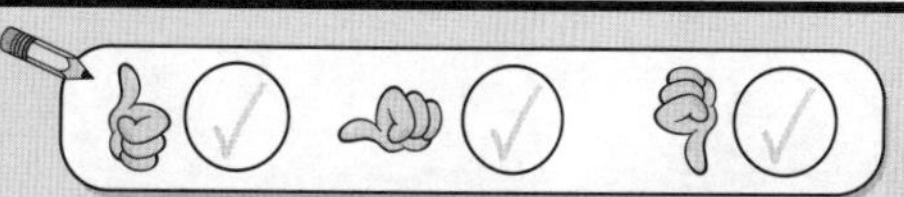

The Mean

1 Fill in the boxes to work out the mean of 2, 4 and 6.

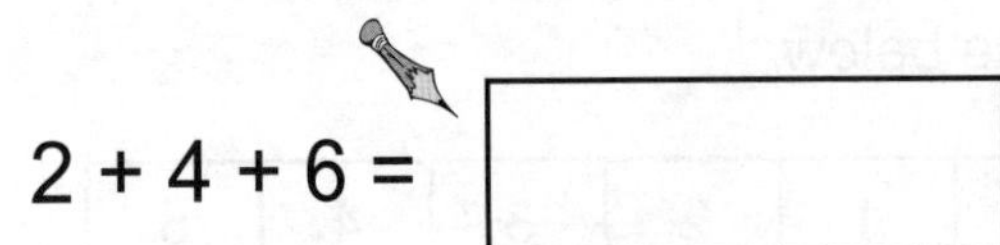

2 + 4 + 6 = ☐

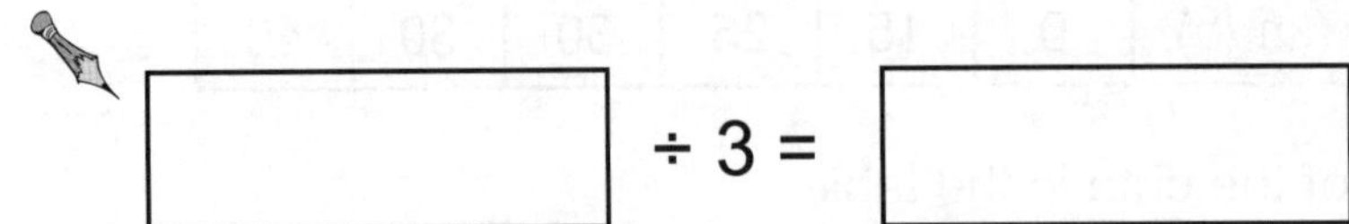

☐ ÷ 3 = ☐

1 mark

2 Calculate the mean of these lists of numbers.

3 5 10

1 mark

2 3 4 7

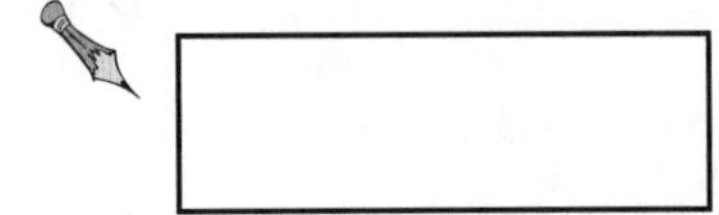

1 mark

3 The mean of the set of numbers below is 3.

What is the missing number?

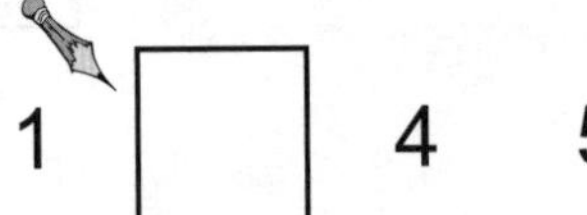

1 ☐ 4 5

1 mark

4 Jesse spends £2 on pens, £1 on chocolate, £5 on hair spray and £12 on T-shirts.

What was the mean cost of the items?

£

1 mark

The Mean

5 This bar chart shows the number of musicals three people have seen.

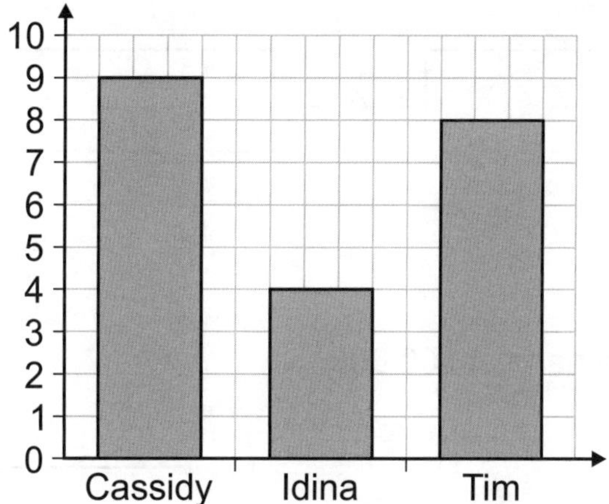

What is the mean number of musicals that they have seen?

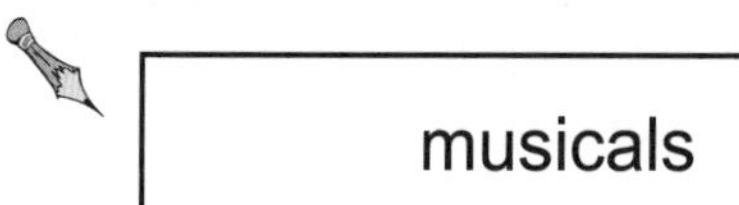

1 mark

6 The scoreboard shows the number of points five children scored in a game of bowling.

Ananta 110
Bourn 60
Carmina 80
Douglas 50
Edwina 100

What is the mean number of points each child scored?

points

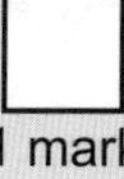

1 mark

"I know what the mean is.
I can calculate and use the mean."

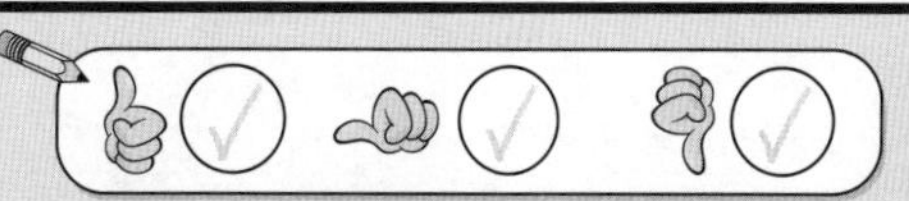

Year Six Objectives Test

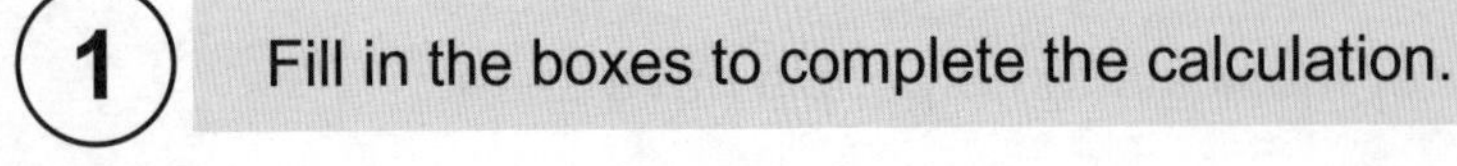

1 Fill in the boxes to complete the calculation.

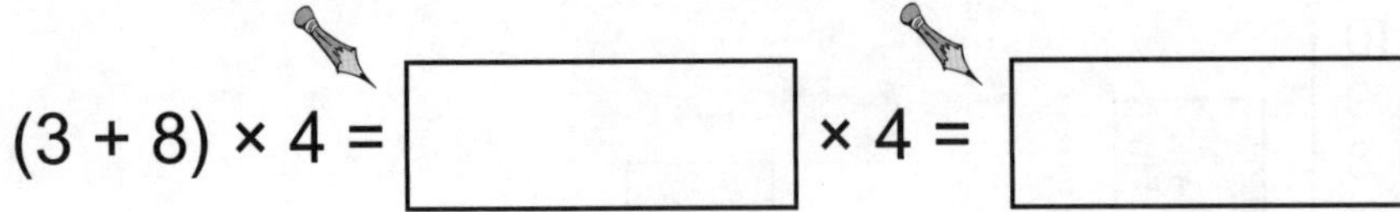

1 mark

2 Round 4 890 326 to the nearest 100 000.

1 mark

3 What is 1307 ÷ 1000?

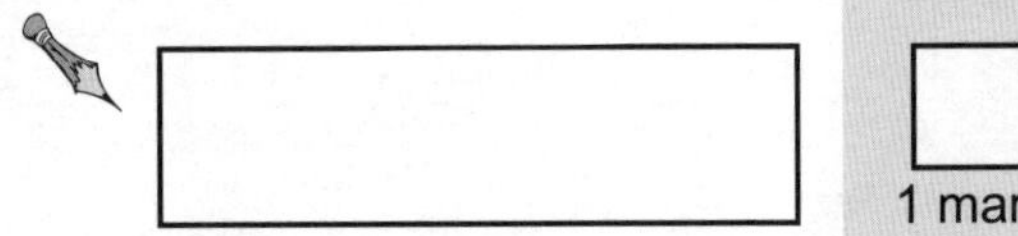

1 mark

4 Half a pineapple costs 60p. How much will 3 whole pineapples cost?

Give your answer in pounds.

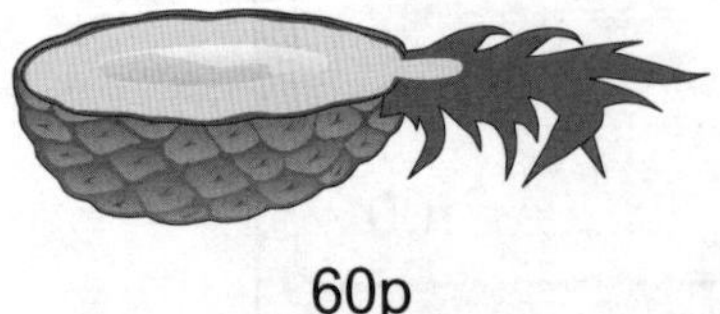

60p

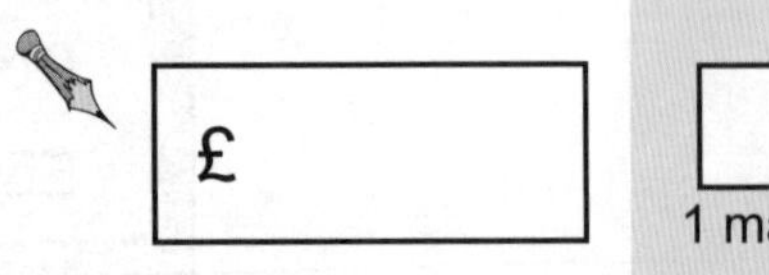

1 mark

5 Write down the next term of the sequence.

8 14 20

1 mark

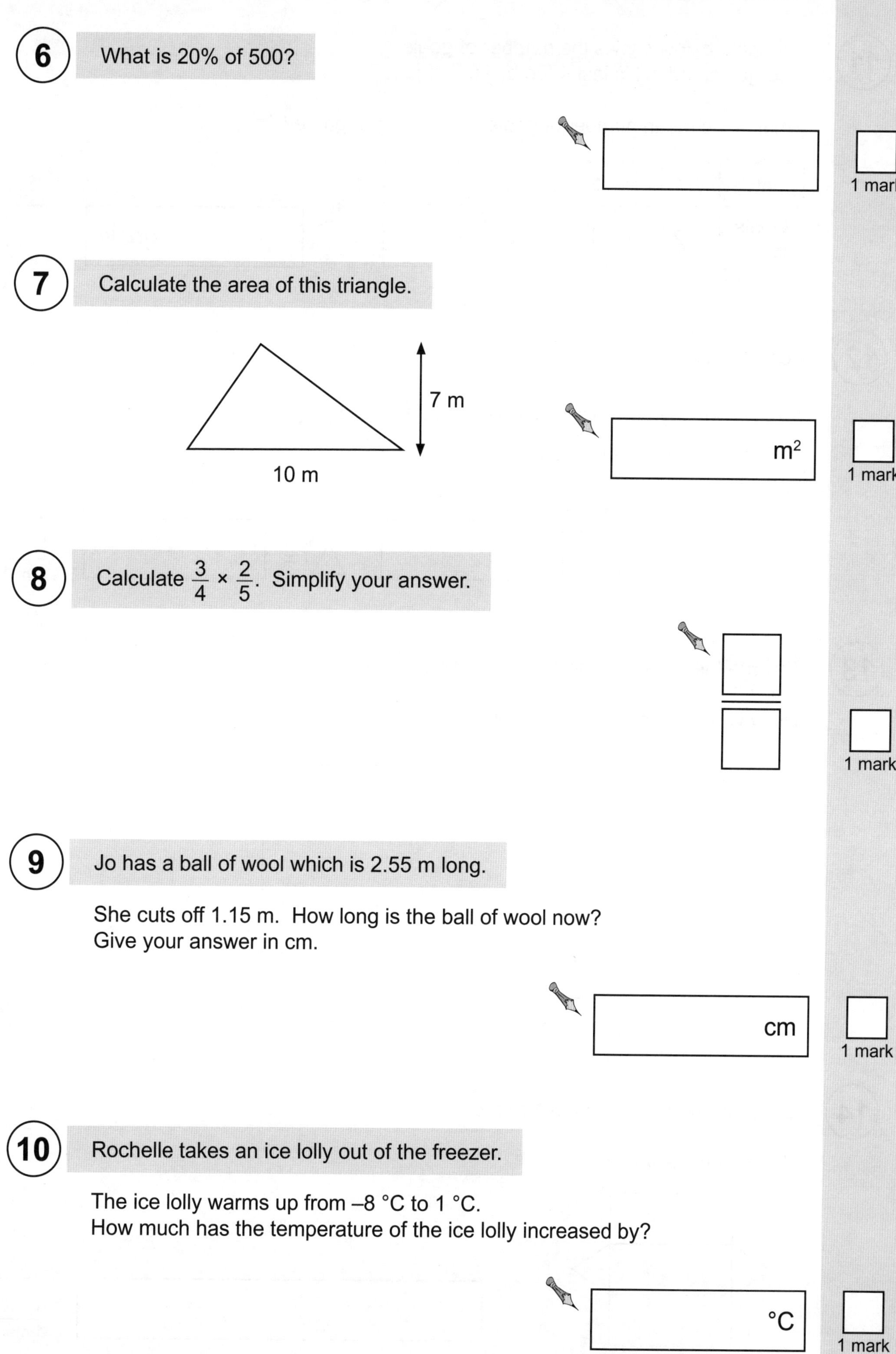

6
What is 20% of 500?
1 mark
7
Calculate the area of this triangle.
7 m
10 m
m²
1 mark
8
Calculate $\frac{3}{4} \times \frac{2}{5}$. Simplify your answer.
1 mark
9
Jo has a ball of wool which is 2.55 m long.
She cuts off 1.15 m. How long is the ball of wool now?
Give your answer in cm.
cm
1 mark
10
Rochelle takes an ice lolly out of the freezer.
The ice lolly warms up from –8 °C to 1 °C.
How much has the temperature of the ice lolly increased by?
°C
1 mark

11 The table below shows the number of goals George scored in his last 4 football matches.

What is the mean number of goals he scored per game?

Match	1	2	3	4
Goals scored	2	1	3	2

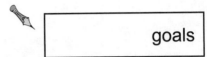

goals

1 mark

12 Look at this equation: ◯ + △ = 6

Write down any possible pair of values for ◯ and △, where ◯ is bigger than △.

◯ = 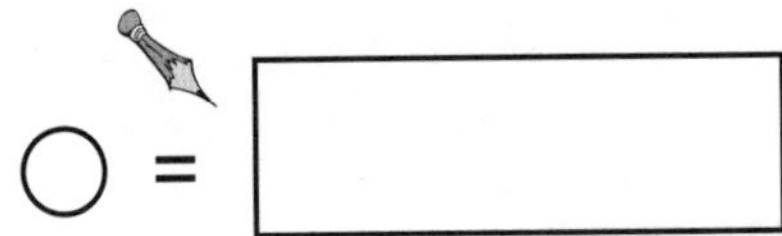 △ = 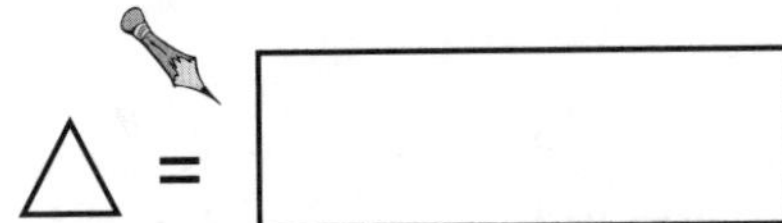

1 mark

13 Enlarge the square below by a scale factor of 4.

Draw your answer on the grid below.

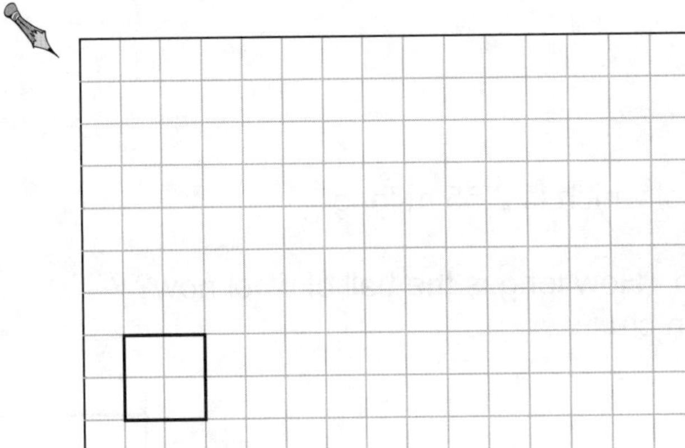

1 mark

14 Jahan draws the net of a 3D shape.

What shape is the net of?

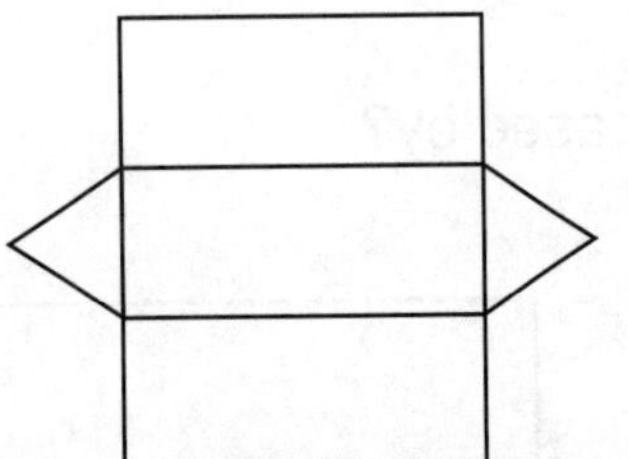

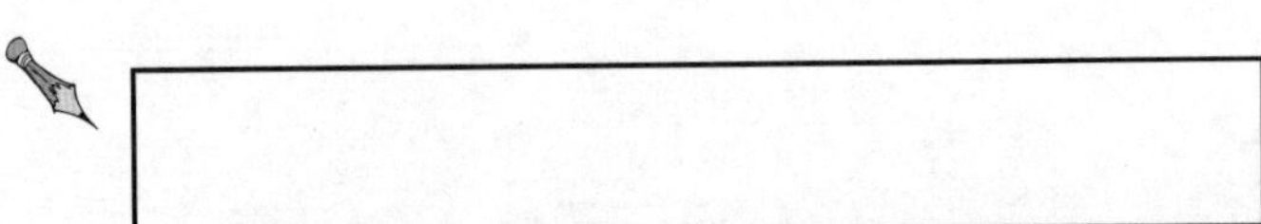

1 mark

15 s represents a number. 5 lots of s equal 60.

Find the value of s.

s = ____ 1 mark

16 Calculate the size of angle a.

a
130°
50°
75°

a = ____ ° 1 mark

17 Beth has plotted 3 points on a grid.

y
4
3
2
1
-4 -3 -2 -1 0 1 2 3 4 x
-1
-2
-3
-4

Put a cross at point (2, –2).
Join the points up to make a kite.

1 mark

Translate your kite 5 units left and 2 units down.

1 mark

18 A group of 15 friends win £6918. They divide the money equally between them. Each friend gets a whole amount.

How much does each friend get? How much money is left over?

2 marks

Total

Answers

Pages 2-5 — Year Five Objectives Test

Q1 **450** should be circled. *(1 mark)*

Q2 20 out of 100 squares are shaded which is **20%**. *(1 mark)*

Q3 **4** *(1 mark)*
–3 *(1 mark)*

Q4 **CL** should be ticked. *(1 mark)*

Q5 9 × 9 = 81, so 81 ÷ **9** = 9 and 810 ÷ **90** = 9 *(1 mark)*

Q6 Her cuboid is made of 16 cubes, so it has a volume of **16 cm³**. *(1 mark)*

Q7
```
  1 5 0 1 7
+ 2 4 9 7 9
  3 9 9 9 6
        1
```
(1 mark)

E.g. Rounding to the nearest 1000:
15 000 + 25 000 *(1 mark)*

Q8 z is 7 m because the opposite side is 7 m. y is 2 m because the opposite side is 2 m. So z is 7 – 2 = **5 m** longer than y. *(1 mark)*

Q9 1000 g = 1 kg, so 9800 ÷ 1000 = **9.8 kg** *(1 mark)*

Q10

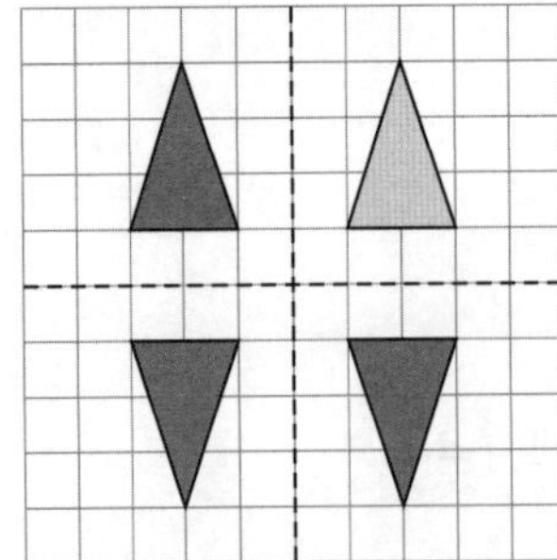

(2 marks — 1 mark for a correct reflection in mirror line 1, 1 mark for a correct reflection of both triangles in mirror line 2)

Q11
```
    1 0 1 2
  ×     3 6
    6 0 7 2
  3 0 3 6 0
  3 6 4 3 2
      1
```
(1 mark)

Q12 360° – 300° = **60°** *(1 mark)*

Q13 In year 3, an adult ticket cost £6 and a child ticket cost £4. So the tickets cost £6 + £4 = **£10** in total. *(1 mark)*

In year 5, an adult ticket cost £7 and a child ticket cost £5. So an adult ticket cost £7 – £5 = **£2** more. *(1 mark)*

Q14 $\frac{1}{4} = \frac{2}{8}$, so
$\frac{3}{8} + \frac{1}{4} = \mathbf{\frac{5}{8}}$ *(1 mark)*

Q15 200 cm = 2 m. 2 m is 2 lots of 1 m, so 2 m ≈ 2 × 3 feet = 6 feet. Rod A is approximately 6 feet, so **Rod B** is shorter. *(2 marks — 1 mark for converting 200 cm to feet or 5 feet to metres, 1 mark for the correct final answer)*

Section One — Number and Place Value

Page 6 — Place Value in Very Large Numbers

Q1 **2** should be circled *(1 mark)*

Q2 **700 000** + 2000 + 90 *(1 mark)*
1 000 000 + **50 000** + 300 *(1 mark)*

Q3 987 300 **>** 963 100 *(1 mark)*
1 154 120 **<** 1 172 200 *(1 mark)*

Q4 **Three million, two hundred and sixty one thousand.** *(1 mark)*

Q5 **1 234 600, 1 412 100, 2 320 900** *(1 mark)*

Page 7 — Rounding Whole Numbers

Q1 **7800, 8100** and **7500** should be circled *(1 mark)*.

Q2 **20 000** *(1 mark)*
150 000 *(1 mark)*
3 150 000 *(1 mark)*

Q3 **500 000** *(1 mark)*

Q4 **6 000 000** *(1 mark)*
6 453 000 *(1 mark)*

Answers

Page 8 — Calculating with Negative Numbers

Q1 **–3** *(1 mark)*
–5 *(1 mark)*

Q2 **–7** and **–2** should be circled. *(1 mark)*

Q3 **1** *(1 mark)*
2 *(1 mark)*

Q4 **–5** *(1 mark)*
–4 *(1 mark)*

Q5 Count on in steps of 1 from –5 to 3.
There are 8 steps, so the difference is **8 °C**.
(1 mark)

Page 9 — Solving Number Problems

Q1 **4 068 037** *(1 mark)*

Q2 –5 – 3 = **–8 points**
(1 mark)
–5 + 9 = **4 points**
(1 mark)

Q3 **Painting C, Painting A, Painting B** *(1 mark)*
£3 000 000 *(1 mark)*
£3 530 000 *(1 mark)*

Section Two — Calculations

Page 10 — Written Multiplication

Q1
$$\begin{array}{r} 1\ 2\ 2 \\ \times\quad 4\ 3 \\ \hline 3\ 6\ 6 \\ 4\ 8\ 8\ 0 \\ \hline \mathbf{5\ 2\ 4\ 6} \\ {\scriptstyle 1\ 1\quad\ \ } \end{array}$$ *(1 mark)*

$$\begin{array}{r} 4\ 2\ 8 \\ \times\quad 3\ 1 \\ \hline 4\ 2\ 8 \\ 1\ 2\ 8_2\ 4\ 0 \\ \hline \mathbf{1\ 3\ 2\ 6\ 8} \\ {\scriptstyle 1\qquad\ } \end{array}$$ *(1 mark)*

Q2
$$\begin{array}{r} 1\ 4\ 0\ 4 \\ \times\quad 5\ 2 \\ \hline 2\ 8\ 0\ 8 \\ 7_2\ 0\ 2_2\ 0\ 0 \\ \hline \mathbf{7\ 3\ 0\ 0\ 8} \\ {\scriptstyle 1\qquad\ } \end{array}$$ *(1 mark)*

$$\begin{array}{r} 3\ 3\ 1\ 4 \\ \times\quad 2\ 6 \\ \hline 1\ 9_1\ 8\ 8_2\ 4 \\ 6\ 6\ 2\ 8\ 0 \\ \hline \mathbf{8\ 6\ 1\ 6\ 4} \\ {\scriptstyle 1\ 1\ 1\quad\ } \end{array}$$ *(1 mark)*

Q3
$$\begin{array}{r} 2\ 1\ 2\ 4 \\ \times\quad 5\ 2 \\ \hline 4\ 2\ 4\ 8 \\ 1\ 0\ 6_1\ 2_2\ 0\ 0 \\ \hline 1\ 1\ 0\ 4\ 4\ 8 \\ {\scriptstyle 1\qquad\quad} \end{array}$$

So he travels **110 448 km**
(2 marks for the correct final answer, 1 mark for an attempt to solve 2124 × 52 with no more than one error)

Page 11 — Written Division

Q1
$$\begin{array}{r} \mathbf{4\ 3} \\ 12\ \overline{)\,5\ 1\ 6} \\ -\underline{4\ 8}\ \ \\ 3\ 6 \\ -\underline{3\ 6} \\ 0 \end{array}$$ *(1 mark)*

$$\begin{array}{r} \mathbf{1\ 1\ 3} \\ 21\ \overline{)\,2\ 3\ 7\ 3} \\ -\underline{2\ 1}\quad\ \ \\ 2\ 7\ \ \\ -\underline{2\ 1}\ \ \\ 6\ 3 \\ -\underline{6\ 3} \\ 0 \end{array}$$ *(1 mark)*

Q2
$$\begin{array}{r} 4\ 2 \\ 15\ \overline{)\,6\ 3\ 5} \\ -\underline{6\ 0}\ \ \\ 3\ 5 \\ -\underline{3\ 0} \\ 5 \end{array}$$ *(1 mark)*

So 635 ÷ 15 = **42 remainder 5** *(1 mark)*

$$\begin{array}{r} 2\ 5\ 4 \\ 13\ \overline{)\,3\ 3\ 0\ 9} \\ -\underline{2\ 6}\quad\ \ \\ 7\ 0\ \ \\ -\underline{6\ 5}\ \ \\ 5\ 9 \\ -\underline{5\ 2} \\ 7 \end{array}$$ *(1 mark)*

So 3309 ÷ 13 = **254 remainder 7** *(1 mark)*

Q3
$$\begin{array}{r} 2\ 2\ 9 \\ 11\ \overline{)\,2\ 5\ 2\ 0} \\ -\underline{2\ 2}\quad\ \ \\ 3\ 2\ \ \\ -\underline{2\ 2}\ \ \\ 1\ 0\ 0 \\ -\underline{\ \ 9\ 9} \\ 1 \end{array}$$ *(1 mark)*

So they can afford **229 textbooks** *(1 mark)*.
They'll have **£1** left *(1 mark)*.

Answers

Page 12 — Mental Maths

Q1 **39 000** *(1 mark)*
27 000 *(1 mark)*

Q2 **72 000** *(1 mark)*
600 *(1 mark)*

Q3 **414 000** should be circled *(1 mark)*

Q4 900 × 7 = **6300 houses** *(1 mark)*

Q5 2800 ÷ 40 = **70 batches** *(1 mark)*

Page 13 — Estimating and Checking

Q1 **180 ÷ 30** should be circled *(1 mark)*
180 ÷ 30 = **6** *(1 mark)*

Q2 **23 000 – 6000** *(1 mark)*

Q3 Rounding each number to the nearest ten thousand:
50 000 + 60 000 + 70 000
= **180 000 fans**
(1 mark)

Q4 Rounding both numbers to the nearest 10 gives
90 × 30 = 2700
which is much higher than 1450, so she is **not right**. *(2 marks — 1 mark for the correct answer, 1 mark for a correct explanation)*

Page 14 — BODMAS

Q1 10 – (9 ÷ 3)
= 10 – **3** = **7** *(1 mark)*
(6 – 4) × 5 = **2** × 5 = **10**
(1 mark)

Q2 7 + 18 ÷ 3 = 7 + 6 = **13**
(1 mark)
9 – 4 × 2 = 9 – 8 = **1**
(1 mark)

Q3 8 + 2 × 9 = 8 + 18 = 26
so Chen is **not** correct.
(2 marks — 1 mark for the correct answer, 1 mark for a correct explanation)

Q4 7 × (4 + **3**) = 49 *(1 mark)*
10 – 12 ÷ 2 = 4 *(1 mark)*

Page 15 — Multiples, Factors and Primes

Q1 **7** and **43** are prime numbers *(1 mark)*
7, **28**, **56** and **77** should all be circled. *(1 mark)*

Q2 **30** and **60** should be ticked. *(1 mark)*

Q3 Factors of 20:
1, 2, 4, 5, 10, 20
Factors of 50:
1, 2, 5, 10, 25, 50
1, **2**, **5** and **10** are common factors.
(1 mark)

Q4 21 and 42 are common multiples less than 50, so there are **2** numbers.
(1 mark)

Q5 Factors of 42:
1, 2, 3, 6, 7, 14, 21, 42
Factors of 60:
1, 2, 3, 4, 5, 6, 10, 12, 15, 20, 30, 60
2 and **3** are the only common factors that are prime. *(1 mark)*

Pages 16-17 — Solving Calculation Problems

Q1 **5 × 12 – 25** should be circled *(1 mark)*.
35 pens *(1 mark)*

Q2 **5 × 8 × 4** should be circled *(1 mark)*.
160 pupils *(1 mark)*

Q3 58 + 92 = 150
150 ÷ 2 = **75 blackberries**
(1 mark)

Q4 10 × 4 = 40, 6 × 3 = 18
40 + 18 = 58
58 ÷ 2 = **29 people**
(1 mark)

Q5 3 × 14 = 42
90 – 42 = 48
48 ÷ 4 = **12 pupils**
(1 mark)

Q6 Dan = 20 points
Raj = 3 × 20 = 60 points
Sky = 180 – 20 – 60
= 100 points
100 – 20 = **80 points**
(1 mark)

Answers

Section Three — Fractions, Decimals and Percentages

Page 18 — Simplifying Fractions

Q1 $8 \div 2 = 4$, $10 \div 2 = 5$
so $\frac{8}{10} = \mathbf{\frac{4}{5}}$ *(1 mark)*

Q2 $\frac{9}{12}$ $\frac{6}{10}$ $\frac{18}{20}$ $\frac{5}{15}$

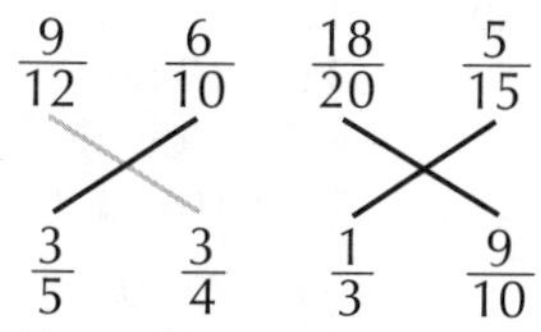

$\frac{3}{5}$ $\frac{3}{4}$ $\frac{1}{3}$ $\frac{9}{10}$
(1 mark)

Q3 $\mathbf{\frac{7}{12}}$ and $\mathbf{\frac{4}{5}}$ should both be circled. *(1 mark)*

Q4 E.g.
$1 \times 3 = 3$, $4 \times 3 = 12$,
so $\frac{1}{4} = \mathbf{\frac{3}{12}}$
$2 \times 4 = 8$, $3 \times 4 = 12$,
so $\frac{2}{3} = \mathbf{\frac{8}{12}}$
(2 marks for two correct equivalent fractions with the same denominator, 1 mark for one correct equivalent fraction)

Page 19 — Ordering Fractions

Q1 $\frac{6}{9} = \mathbf{\frac{2}{3}}$

$\frac{2}{6} = \mathbf{\frac{1}{3}}$
(1 mark for both correct)

$\mathbf{\frac{6}{9}}$ is larger. *(1 mark)*

Q2 $\frac{1}{4} = \mathbf{\frac{5}{20}}$

$\frac{7}{10} = \mathbf{\frac{14}{20}}$

$\frac{2}{5} = \frac{\mathbf{8}}{20}$
(1 mark for correct numerators)

So the order is:
$\mathbf{\frac{1}{4}}, \mathbf{\frac{2}{5}}, \mathbf{\frac{7}{10}}$ *(1 mark)*

Q3 $1\frac{1}{5} = \frac{5}{5} + \frac{1}{5} = \frac{6}{5}$

So the order is:
$\mathbf{\frac{11}{5}}, \mathbf{\frac{8}{5}}, \mathbf{1\frac{1}{5}}$ *(1 mark)*

Pages 20-21 — Adding and Subtracting Fractions

Q1 $\frac{2}{5} = \frac{4}{10}$

$\frac{4}{10} + \frac{3}{10} = \mathbf{\frac{7}{10}}$
(1 mark)

$\frac{1}{4} = \frac{2}{8}$

$\frac{7}{8} - \frac{2}{8} = \mathbf{\frac{5}{8}}$ *(1 mark)*

Q2 $\frac{1}{4} = \frac{3}{12}$ so

$\frac{5}{12} + \frac{3}{12} = \mathbf{\frac{8}{12}} = \mathbf{\frac{2}{3}}$
(1 mark)

$\frac{2}{3} = \frac{4}{6}$ so

$\frac{4}{6} - \frac{1}{6} = \mathbf{\frac{3}{6}} = \mathbf{\frac{1}{2}}$
(1 mark)

Q3 $\frac{3}{2} = \frac{12}{8}$

$\frac{5}{8} + \frac{12}{8} = \frac{17}{8}$
so $\mathbf{\frac{17}{8}}$ should be circled.
(1 mark)

Q4 $\frac{1}{3} = \frac{3}{9}$

$\frac{3}{9} + \frac{5}{9} = \frac{8}{9}$

so $\mathbf{\frac{8}{9}}$ of the popcorn is eaten. *(1 mark)*

Q5 $\frac{1}{2} + \frac{2}{5} = \mathbf{\frac{5}{10}} + \mathbf{\frac{4}{10}}$
$= \mathbf{\frac{9}{10}}$
(2 marks — 1 mark for the correct equivalent fractions, 1 mark for the correct final answer)

$\frac{3}{4} - \frac{3}{5} = \mathbf{\frac{15}{20}} - \mathbf{\frac{12}{20}}$
$= \mathbf{\frac{3}{20}}$
(2 marks — 1 mark for the correct equivalent fractions, 1 mark for the correct final answer)

Q6 $\frac{2}{3} = \frac{6}{9}$, so $1\frac{2}{3} + \frac{2}{9}$
$= 1\frac{6}{9} + \frac{2}{9} = \mathbf{1\frac{8}{9}}$
(1 mark)

Q7 $\frac{1}{3} = \frac{4}{12}$

$1 - \frac{7}{12} - \frac{4}{12} = \frac{1}{12}$

so $\mathbf{\frac{1}{12}}$ of the water balloons have not been thrown. *(1 mark)*

Q8 $\frac{3}{5} + \frac{1}{6} = \frac{18}{30} + \frac{5}{30}$
$= \mathbf{\frac{23}{30}}$ *(1 mark)*

Page 22 — Multiplying Fractions

Q1 $\frac{1}{2} \times \frac{1}{5} = \mathbf{\frac{1}{10}}$ *(1 mark)*

$\frac{1}{3} \times \frac{1}{6} = \mathbf{\frac{1}{18}}$ *(1 mark)*

$\frac{3}{5} \times \frac{1}{4} = \mathbf{\frac{3}{20}}$ *(1 mark)*

$\frac{1}{2} \times \frac{5}{6} = \mathbf{\frac{5}{12}}$ *(1 mark)*

Q2 $\frac{1}{2} \times \frac{4}{5} = \frac{4}{10} = \frac{2}{5}$
so $\mathbf{\frac{2}{5}}$ should be circled.
(1 mark)

Q3 $\frac{2}{3} \times \frac{8}{10} = \frac{16}{30} = \mathbf{\frac{8}{15}}$
(1 mark)

Answers

Page 23 — Dividing Fractions by Whole Numbers

Q1 $\frac{1}{2} \div 3 = \mathbf{\frac{1}{6}}$ *(1 mark)*

$\frac{1}{4} \div 5 = \mathbf{\frac{1}{20}}$ *(1 mark)*

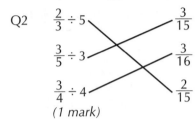

Q2

$\frac{2}{3} \div 5$	$\frac{3}{15}$
$\frac{3}{5} \div 3$	$\frac{3}{16}$
$\frac{3}{4} \div 4$	$\frac{2}{15}$

(1 mark)

Q3 $\frac{6}{15} \div 4 = \frac{6}{60} = \mathbf{\frac{1}{10}}$
(1 mark)

Q4 $\frac{1}{2} \div 6 = \frac{1}{12}$,
so each person gets
$\mathbf{\frac{1}{12}}$ of the whole pie.
(1 mark)

Page 24 — Multiplying or Dividing by 10, 100 or 1000

Q1

$2.4\underline{5}$	five thousandths
$0.11\underline{5}$	five tenths
$3.\underline{5}07$	five hundredths

(2 marks for all correct, 1 mark for one or two correct)

Q2 63.1 **×** 100 = 6310
(1 mark)
42 **÷** 1000 = 0.042
(1 mark)

Q3 4.21 ÷ 10 = **0.421**
(1 mark)
1.845 × 100 = **184.5**
(1 mark)

Q4 $0.9\underline{2} \times 10 = 9.\underline{2}$
So the value of the underlined digit is **two tenths** or **0.2**. *(1 mark)*

$1.\underline{2}3 \times 1000 = 1\underline{2}30$
So the value of the underlined digit is **two hundreds** or **200**.
(1 mark)

Page 25 – Multiplying with Decimals

Q1 4 × 3 = **12**
4 is 10 times larger than 0.4, so divide by 10.
12 ÷ 10 = 1.2
So 0.4 × 3 = **1.2**
(1 mark for both numbers correct)

Q2 2 × 7 = 14
2 is 10 times larger than 0.2, so divide by 10.
14 ÷ 10 = **1.4** *(1 mark)*

8 × 6 = 48
8 is 10 times larger than 0.8, so divide by 10.
48 ÷ 10 = **4.8** *(1 mark)*

Q3 13 × 2 = 26
13 is 10 times larger than 1.3, so divide by 10.
26 ÷ 10 = **2.6** *(1 mark)*

22 × 4 = 88
22 is 10 times larger than 2.2, so divide by 10.
88 ÷ 10 = **8.8** *(1 mark)*

6 × 6 = 36
6 is 100 times larger than 0.06, so divide by 100.
36 ÷ 100 = **0.36** *(1 mark)*

Q4
```
   8 9
×    5
 4 4 5
   4
```
89 is 100 times larger than 0.89, so divide by 100. 445 ÷ 100 = **4.45**
(1 mark)

Page 26 — Dividing with Decimals

Q1 68 ÷ 2 = **34**
68 is 10 times larger than 6.8, so divide by 10.
34 ÷ 10 = 3.4
So 6.8 ÷ 2 = **3.4**
(1 mark for both numbers correct)

Q2 33 ÷ 3 = 11
33 is 10 times larger than 3.3, so divide by 10.
11 ÷ 10 = **1.1** *(1 mark)*

63 ÷ 7 = 9
63 is 10 times larger than 6.3, so divide by 10.
9 ÷ 10 = **0.9** *(1 mark)*

Q3
```
   3 6
6|2 1 ³6
```
216 is 10 times larger than 21.6, so divide by 10. 36 ÷ 10 = **3.6**
(1 mark)
```
   1 7
9|1 5 ⁶3
```
153 is 100 times larger than 1.53, so divide by 100. 17 ÷ 100 = **0.17**
(1 mark)

Q4 24 ÷ 4 = 6
24 is 10 times larger than 2.4, so divide by 10.
6 ÷ 10 = **0.6 litres**
(1 mark)

Page 27 — Rounding Decimals

Q1 2.11 → **2.1** *(1 mark)*
3.55 → **3.6** *(1 mark)*

Q2 5.938 → **5.9** *(1 mark)*
1.062 → **1.1** *(1 mark)*

Q3 3.653 → **3.65** *(1 mark)*
2.906 → **2.91** *(1 mark)*

Q4 1.41 + 1.41 = 2.82
2.82 to 1 decimal place is **2.8 m** *(1 mark)*

Q5 7.96 to the nearest 1 decimal place is 8.0, so **7.96 kg** should be circled. *(1 mark)*

Answers

Pages 28-29 — Fractions, Decimals and Percentages

Q1 $\mathbf{\frac{6}{10}}$ *(1 mark)* and **60%** *(1 mark)*

Q2 $0.15 = \mathbf{\frac{15}{100}} = \mathbf{15\%}$ *(1 mark)*

$\frac{20}{25} = \mathbf{\frac{80}{100}} = \mathbf{80\%}$ *(1 mark)*

Q3

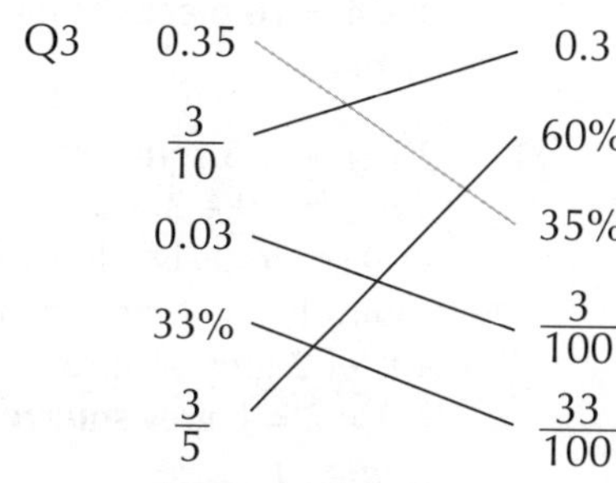

(2 marks for all correct, 1 mark for two or three correct)

Q4

Decimal	Percentage	Fraction
0.2	20%	$\frac{1}{5}$
0.7	70%	$\frac{7}{10}$
0.15	15%	$\frac{3}{20}$

(3 marks — 1 mark for each correct row)

Q5 $8\overline{)1\;0\;{}^{2}0\;{}^{4}0}$ = **125** *(1 mark)*

$125 \div 1000 = \mathbf{0.125}$ *(1 mark)*

Q6 E.g. $\frac{30}{50} = \frac{60}{100} = 60\%$

60% is larger than 45%, so **Selena** has climbed the furthest.

(2 marks — 1 mark for converting so that both amounts are fractions or percentages, 1 mark for the correct final answer)

Section Four — Ratio and Proportion

Pages 30-31 — Relative Sizes

Q1 After 7 weeks there will be 3 × 7 = **21 ripe tomatoes**. *(1 mark)*

Q2 50 × 4 = 200p = **£2** *(1 mark)*

Q3 24 carrot sticks is 4 lots of 6, so 4 lots of 1 day = **4 days**. *(1 mark)*

Q4 £1.50 = 150p
150 ÷ 5 = **30p** *(1 mark)*

Q5 20 football shirts is 5 lots of 4 shirts. So 5 lots of 1 red football shirt = **5 shirts**. *(1 mark)*

Q6 1 alarm clock costs £30 ÷ **6** = **£5** *(1 mark)* so 4 alarm clocks cost 4 × **£5** = **£20** *(1 mark)*

Q7 27 people is 9 lots of 3 people. So 9 lots of 2 people = 9 × 2 = **18 people** prefer chocolate. *(1 mark)*

Q8 32 times is 4 lots of 8. So 4 lots of £40 = **£160**. *(1 mark)*

Pages 32-33 — Scale Factors

Q1

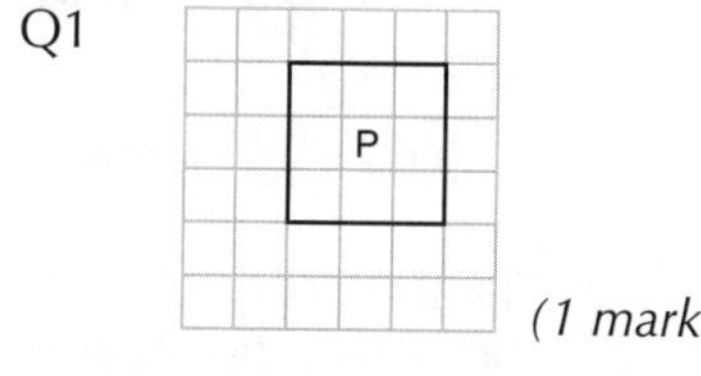

(1 mark)

Q2

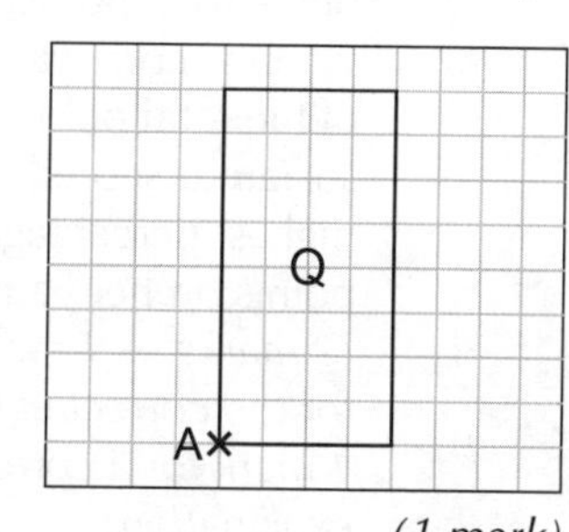

(1 mark)

Q3 Scale factor = **4** *(1 mark)*

Q4

W
A

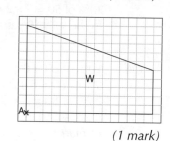

(1 mark)

Q5 6 ÷ 2 = 3, so scale factor = **3** *(1 mark)*

15 ÷ 3 = 5, so scale factor = **5** *(1 mark)*

Q6 30 × a = 300 cm, so a = 300 ÷ 10 = **30 cm** *(1 mark)*

Pages 34-35 — Percentages of Amounts

Q1 10% of 150 = 150 ÷ 10 = 15. So **15** should be circled. *(1 mark)*

Q2 10% of 450 = 450 ÷ 10 = **45** *(1 mark)*, so 20% of 450 = 45 × 2 = **90** *(1 mark)*

Q3

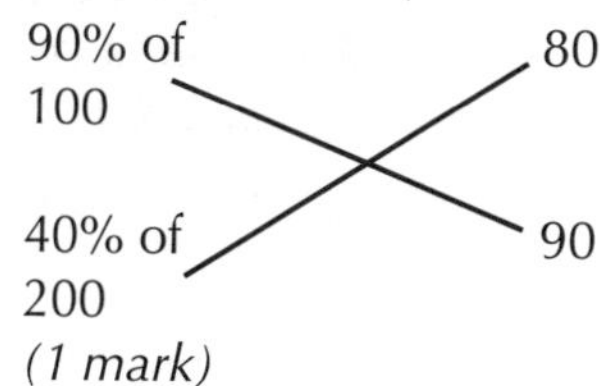

(1 mark)

Q4 10% of 100 = 10,
30% of 100 = 10 × 3 = **30** *(1 mark)*

10% of 220 = 22,
50% of 220 = 22 × 5 = **110** *(1 mark)*

10% of 500 = 50,
40% of 500 = 50 × 4 = **200** *(1 mark)*

10% of 300 = 30,
90% of 300 = 30 × 9 = **270** *(1 mark)*

Answers

Q5 10% of 50 = 5,
20% of 50 = 5 × 2 = 10,
so she sells **10 pairs**.
(1 mark)

Q6 10% of 80 = 8
5% of 80 = 8 ÷ 2 = 4
25% of 80 = 8 + 8 + 4
= 20, so Adam pays **£20**.
(1 mark)

Q7 10% of 200 = 20,
5% of 200 = 20 ÷ 2 = **10**
(1 mark)

10% of 900 = 90,
5% of 900 = 90 ÷ 2 = 45
So 15% of 900 = 90 + 45
= **135** *(1 mark)*

Q8 10% of 250 = 25,
70% of 250 = 25 × 7
= 175, so he uses **175 ml** of cream. *(1 mark)*

Q9 10% of 30 = 3,
50% of 30 = 3 × 5
= 15 mini doughnuts.
10% of 20 = 2,
70% of 20 = 2 × 7
= 14 mini doughnuts.
Frank eats 15 mini doughnuts and Lesley eats 14, so **Frank** eats more mini doughnuts.
(2 marks — 1 mark for the correct answer, 1 mark for a correct explanation)

Pages 36-37 — Comparing Using Percentages

Q1 $\frac{10}{20} = \frac{50}{100} =$ **50%**
(1 mark)

Q2 $\frac{£30}{£50} = \frac{60}{100} =$ **60%**
(1 mark)

Q3 $\frac{60}{300} = \frac{20}{100} =$ **20%**
(1 mark)

Q4 $\frac{5}{25} = \frac{20}{100} = 20\%$,
100% – 20% = **80% of the sand castles** are left.
(1 mark)

Q5 10% of 50 = 5
30% of 50 = 5 × 3 = 15
50 – 15 = 35, so he has **35 balloons** left. *(1 mark)*

Q6 40 + 25 + 35 = 100,
$\frac{40}{100} = 40\%$, so **40%** of the cupcakes have stars.
(1 mark)

Q7 $\frac{£5}{£50} = \frac{10}{100} = 10\%$

$\frac{£5}{£25} = \frac{20}{100} = 20\%$

$\frac{£20}{£200} = \frac{10}{100} = 10\%$

So the middle label should be circled:

(1 mark)

Q8 Tamar:
$\frac{360}{400} = \frac{90}{100} = 90\%$
Jacob:
$\frac{400}{500} = \frac{80}{100} = 80\%$

Tamar's score was 90% of the total points and Jacob's score was 80% of the total points, so **Tamar** scored the highest percentage of points on her game.
(2 marks — 1 mark for the correct answer, 1 mark for a correct explanation)

Pages 38-39 — Unequal Sharing

Q1 There are 3 × 5
= **15 red jelly beans**
(1 mark)

Q2 For every **2 rabbits** there are **3 ducks**. *(1 mark)*
If there were 4 rabbits, there would be **6 ducks**.
(1 mark)

Q3 12 ÷ 3 = 4, so there are 4 × 4 = **16 pieces** of ham.
(1 mark)

Q4 2 in every 3 squirrels are grey. 9 ÷ 3 = 3, so 9 squirrels is 3 lots of 3 squirrels. So there are 3 lots of 2 grey squirrels = 3 × 2 = **6 grey squirrels**.
(1 mark)

Q5 10 blueberries is 5 lots of 2 blueberries. So Jaydene has 5 lots of 3 blueberries = 5 × 3 = **15 blueberries.**
(1 mark)

Q6 4 in every 10 people are women. 50 ÷ 10 = 5, so 50 people is 5 lots of 10 people. So there are 5 lots of 4 women = 5 × 4 = **20 women** *(1 mark)*, and 5 lots of 6 men = 5 × 6 = **30 men**.
(1 mark)

Answers

Section Five — Algebra

Pages 40-41 — Sequences

Q1 1, 3, 5, 7, **9**, **11** *(1 mark)*

Q2 20, 17, 14, 11, **8**, **5** *(1 mark)*

Q3 7 – 3 = 4
11 – 7 = 4
15 – 11 = 4
So the rule is add **4**. *(1 mark)*
15 + 4 = **19** *(1 mark)*

Q4 The rule is add 5, so the next term is **17** *(1 mark)*

Q5 The rule is subtract 6, so the next term is **7** *(1 mark)*

Q6 E.g. 6 – 1 = 5, 11 – 6 = 5
So the rule is **add 5**. *(1 mark)*
E.g. 17 – 10 = 7, 24 – 17 = 7
So the rule is **add 7**. *(1 mark)*
E.g. 14 – 18 = –4, 10 – 14 = –4
So the rule is **subtract 4**. *(1 mark)*

Q7 The rule is subtract 8, so the sequences are:
43, 35, **27**, **19**, 11, 3 *(1 mark)*
38, 30, **22**, 14, 6, **–2** *(1 mark)*

Q8 E.g. 34 – 23 = 11, 45 – 34 = 11
So the rule is add 11.
The first term is 23 – 11 = **12**.
The final term is 56 + 11 = **67**. *(1 mark)*

Pages 42-43 — Missing Number Problems

Q1 △ = 8 – **5** = **3** *(1 mark)*
◯ = 3 + **12** = **15** *(1 mark)*

Q2 2 × ⬠ = 12
So ⬠ = 12 ÷ 2
= **6** *(1 mark)*

Q3 ☆ = 19 – 7 = **12** *(1 mark)*
✫ = 18 ÷ 3 = **6** *(1 mark)*

Q4 10 + 4 = 14
14 ÷ 2 = **7** *(1 mark)*
30 ÷ 3 = 10
10 + 5 = **15** *(1 mark)*

Q5 13 – 3 = 10
10 ÷ 5 = 2
So p = **2** *(1 mark)*

Q6 **7t = 56** should be circled. *(1 mark)*
t = 56 ÷ 7 = **8** *(1 mark)*

Q7 **y + 2y = 30** should be circled. *(1 mark)*
3y = 30
so y = 30 ÷ 3 = **10** *(1 mark)*

Pages 44-45 — Two Missing Numbers

Q1 **◯ + □ = 7** should be circled. *(1 mark)*

Q2 **△ = 3 ▽ = 1**
△ = 5 ▽ = 3
(1 mark for both correct)

Q3 1 + b = 5 so b = **4** *(1 mark)*
a + 2 = 5 so a = **3** *(1 mark)*

Q4 Some possible pairs are:
m = 1 n = 9
m = 2 n = 8
m = 3 n = 7
m = 4 n = 6
m = 5 n = 5
(1 mark for any correct pair)

Q5 i = 20 j = 1
i = 10 j = 2
i = 5 j = 4
(2 marks for all pairs correct, 1 mark for one or two pairs correct)

Q6 f = 18 g = 1
f = 9 g = 2
f = 6 g = 3
(2 marks for all pairs correct, 1 mark for one or two pairs correct)

Q7 **E = 3 + D** should be circled. *(1 mark)*

Q8 R = 6 S = 1
R = 4 S = 2
R = 2 S = 3
(2 marks for all pairs correct, 1 mark for one or two pairs correct)

Answers

Pages 46-47 — Formulas

Q1 number of stripes
= 10 × 5 = **50 stripes**
(1 mark)

Q2 number of blades
= 4 × 9 = **36 blades**
(1 mark)

Q3 total cost = 50 + 2 × 12
= 50 + 24 = **£74** *(1 mark)*

Q4 number of diners
= (7 × 10) + 5 = **75 diners**
(1 mark)

Q5 length = 60 + (3 × 25)
= 60 + 75 = **135 minutes**
(1 mark)

Q6 number of wheels
= **12 × number of lorries**
(1 mark)
spare mirrors =
number of lorries ÷ 2 – 5
(1 mark)

Q7 time spent revising
= **1** + (number of tests × **2**) *(1 mark)*

1 + (2 × 5) = 1 + 10
= **11 hours** *(1 mark)*

Section Six — Measurement

Pages 48-49 — Units

Q1 **1050 cm** should be circled *(1 mark)*

Q2 570 g = 570 ÷ 1000
= **0.57 kg** *(1 mark)*
7.25 litres = 7.25 × 1000
= **7250 ml** *(1 mark)*

Q3 8.52 m = 8.52 × 100
= **852 cm** *(1 mark)*
852 cm = 852 × 10
= **8520 mm** *(1 mark)*

Q4 0.35 litres = 0.35 × 1000
= 350 ml
350 – 120 = **230 ml**
(1 mark)

Q5 32 × 200 = 6400 g
6400 g = 6400 ÷ 1000
= **6.4 kg** *(1 mark)*

Q6 10 miles ≈ (10 ÷ 5) × 8
= **16 km** *(1 mark)*
50 miles ≈ (50 ÷ 5) × 8
= **80 km** *(1 mark)*
64 km ≈ (64 ÷ 8) × 5
= **40 miles** *(1 mark)*

Q7 3 litres = 3000 ml
3000 ÷ 200 = **15 days**
(1 mark)

Q8 Each week he feeds it
25 × 7 = 175 g
So in 10 weeks he feeds it
175 × 10 = 1750 g
1750 ÷ 1000 = **1.75 kg**
(2 marks — 1 mark for finding 1750 g, 1 mark for the correct final answer)

Page 50 — Area of a Triangle

Q1 $\frac{1}{2}$ × **8** × **3** = **12 cm²**
(1 mark)

Q2 $\frac{1}{2}$ × 10 × 6 = **30 cm²**
(1 mark)
$\frac{1}{2}$ × 11 × 8 = **44 m²**
(1 mark)

Q3 $\frac{1}{2}$ × 6 × 3 = **9 cm²**
(1 mark)
$\frac{1}{2}$ × 4 × 5 = **10 cm²**
(1 mark)

Page 51 — Area of a Parallelogram

Q1 Area = **Base × Height**
(1 mark)

Q2 10 × 4 = **40 cm²** *(1 mark)*
11 × 2 = **22 m²** *(1 mark)*

Q3 Area of one parallelogram:
9 × 3 = 27 cm²
Area of whole logo:
27 × 3 = **81 cm²**
(2 marks — 1 mark for finding area of one parallelogram, 1 mark for finding area of whole logo)

Answers

Page 52 — Perimeters and Areas

Q1 $4 \times 3 = 12$ cm²
$5 \times 2 = 10$ cm²
So the **4 cm by 3 cm** rectangle should be circled. *(1 mark)*

Q2 Rectangle A:
$4 + 15 + 4 + 15 = 38$ cm
Rectangle B:
$10 + 6 + 10 + 6 = 32$ cm
Rectangle C:
$5 + 12 + 5 + 12 = 34$ cm
So the correct order is **B, C, A**.
(2 marks — 1 mark for finding the perimeter of at least two rectangles, 1 mark for the correct final answer)

Q3 Area of rectangle X:
$9 \times 8 = 72$ cm²
Length of side t:
$72 \div 6 =$ **12 cm**
(2 marks — 1 mark for finding area of rectangle X, 1 mark for finding length of side t)

Page 53 — Volumes of Cubes and Cuboids

Q1 **12 cm³** *(1 mark)*
24 cm³ *(1 mark)*

Q2 Volume = **5 × 5 × 5**
= **125 cm³** *(1 mark)*

Q3 $12 \times 8 \times 5 =$ **480 m³**
(1 mark)

Q4 Volume of crate B:
$10 \times 3 \times 6 = 180$ m³
$180 > 160$ so **crate B** has a larger volume.
(2 marks — 1 mark for the correct answer, 1 mark for correct working)

Section Seven — Geometry

Pages 54-55 — Drawing 2D Shapes

Q1 Drawing of a square with four sides of length **5 cm** and four **90° angles**.
(1 mark)

Q2 Drawing of a triangle with a correct **90° angle** and side lengths of **3 cm** and **4 cm** and an **adjoining side of 5 cm**.
(1 mark)

Q3 Drawing of a trapezium with two **90° angles** and side lengths of **10 cm**, **4 cm** and **6 cm** and **adjoining side of 5.6** or **5.7 cm**. *(1 mark)*

Q4 Drawing of a kite with correct **110°** and **90° angles** and **missing 50° angle**. Sides of length **3 cm**, **3 cm**, **5 cm** and **5 cm**. *(1 mark)*

Pages 56-57 — Making 3D Shapes

Q1

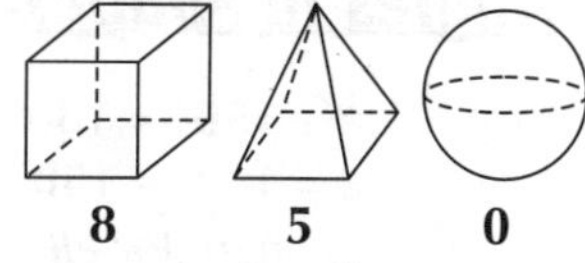

8 **5** **0**

(2 marks for all correct, 1 mark for one or two correct)

Q2 **tetrahedron**, **cylinder** and **cone** should all be circled.
(2 marks for all correct, 1 mark for two correct)

Q3

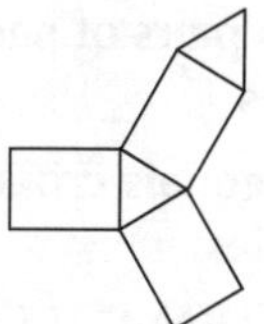

(1 mark)

Q4 (Square-based) **pyramid**
(1 mark)

Q5 Each square face should have an area of 4 cm squares.
E.g.

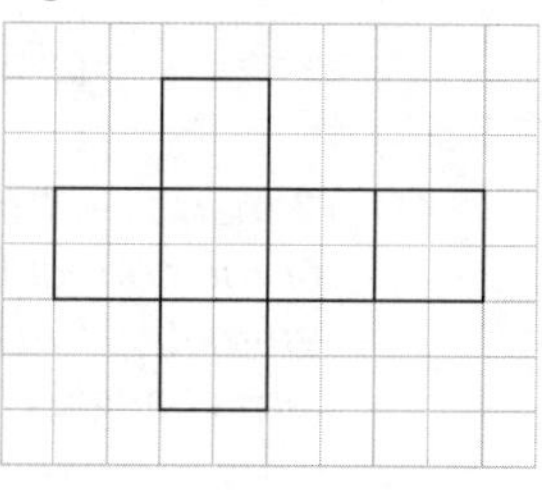

(1 mark)

Q6 E.g.

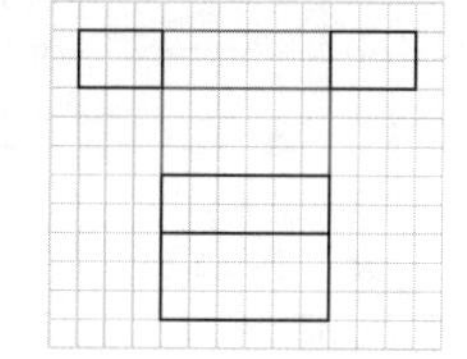

(1 mark)

E.g.

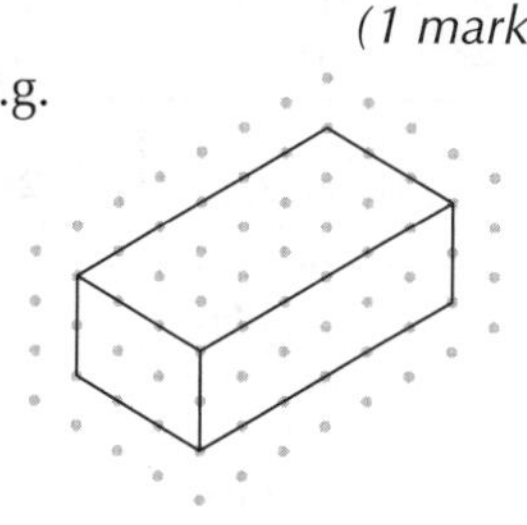

(1 mark)

Pages 58-59 — Shape Properties

Q1

	Not a quadrilateral	Quadrilateral
Sides are all equal lengths	**equilateral triangle**	**square**
Sides are not all equal lengths	**scalene triangle**	**parallelogram**

(2 marks for all correct, 1 mark for three correct)

Answers

Q2 **Two pairs of parallel sides**

Diagonals cross at right angles

(2 marks — 1 mark for each correct answer ticked)

Q3

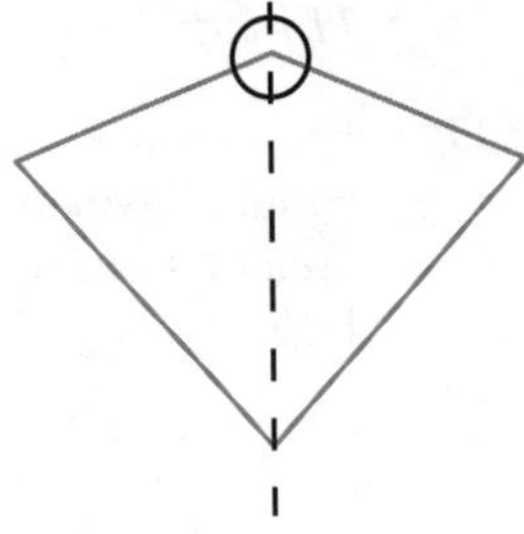

(2 marks — 1 mark for the correct line of symmetry, 1 mark for the correct angle circled)

Q4

Shape	Name	Numbers of lines of symmetry	Pairs of parallel sides
	regular hexagon	**6**	3
	equilateral triangle	3	**0**
	rectangle	**2**	2
	regular octagon	8	4

(2 marks for all correct, 1 mark for two or three correct)

Q5

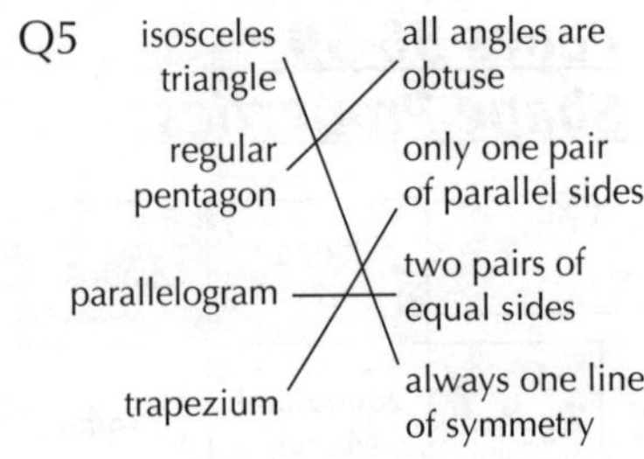

(2 marks for all correct, 1 mark for any two or three correct)

Pages 60-61 — Circles

Q1 E.g.

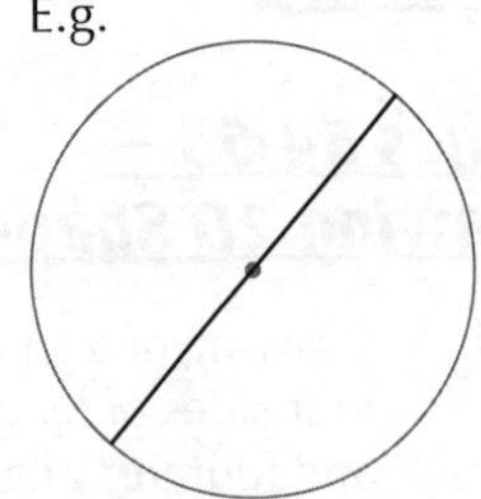

(1 mark for any straight line between points on the circumference through the centre)

Q2 **13 cm** *(1 mark)*
2 cm *(1 mark)*

Q3 **2 cm** *(1 mark)*
3.5 cm *(1 mark)*

Q4 $d = 2 \times r = 2 \times 5$
$= \mathbf{10\ cm}$ *(1 mark)*

Q5 $d = 2 \times r = 2 \times 12$
$= \mathbf{24\ mm}$ *(1 mark)*

Q6 $d = 2 \times r$
$r = d \div 2 = 60 \div 2$
$= \mathbf{30\ cm}$ *(1 mark)*

Q7 $d = 2 \times r$
$r = d \div 2 = 8 \div 2$
$= \mathbf{4\ m}$ *(1 mark)*

Pages 62-63 — Angles in Shapes

Q1 $a + \mathbf{150°} = 180°$
$a = 180° - \mathbf{150°} = \mathbf{30°}$
(1 mark for all correct)

Q2 $b + \mathbf{300°} = 360°$
$b = 360° - \mathbf{300°} = \mathbf{60°}$
(1 mark for all correct)

Q3 $c = 180° - 35° - 90°$
$= \mathbf{55°}$ *(1 mark)*

Q4 $d = 360° - 130°$
$- 70° - 55° = \mathbf{105°}$
(1 mark)

Q5 $e = \mathbf{70°}$ *(1 mark)* because base angles are equal in an isosceles triangle.
So $f = 180° - 70° - 70°$
$= 180° - \mathbf{140°}$
$= \mathbf{40°}$
(1 mark for both correct)

Q6 exterior angle =
$360° \div \mathbf{6} = \mathbf{60°}$
(1 mark for both)
interior angle =
$180° - \mathbf{60°} = \mathbf{120°}$
(1 mark for both correct)

Pages 64-65 — Angle Rules

Q1 $p = \mathbf{69°}$ as the angle is vertically opposite 69°.
(1 mark)

Q2 $q = 180° - 45° - 60°$
$= \mathbf{75°}$ *(1 mark)*

Q3 $r = 360° - 200° - 52°$
$= \mathbf{108°}$ *(1 mark)*

Q4 $s = 360° - 90° - 120°$
$- 35° = \mathbf{115°}$
(1 mark)

Q5 Angle **u** is vertically opposite the 114° angle.
Angle **t** is on a straight line with the 114° angle.
(1 mark for both correct)
So angle $t = 180° - 114°$
$= \mathbf{66°}$
and angle $u = \mathbf{114°}$.
(1 mark for both correct)

Q6 $v + \mathbf{320°} = 360°$
So $v = 360° - 320° = \mathbf{40°}$
(1 mark for both correct)
$w + v + \mathbf{90°} = 180°$
So $w = 180° - 40° - 90°$
$= \mathbf{50°}$
(1 mark for both correct)

Answers

Pages 66-67 — Coordinates

Q1 **–3** *(1 mark)*
–2 *(1 mark)*

Q2 P = **(2, 3)** *(1 mark)*
Q = **(–4, 1)** *(1 mark)*

Q3 **L** *(1 mark)*
J *(1 mark)*

Q4

(2 marks — 1 mark for each point)

Q5

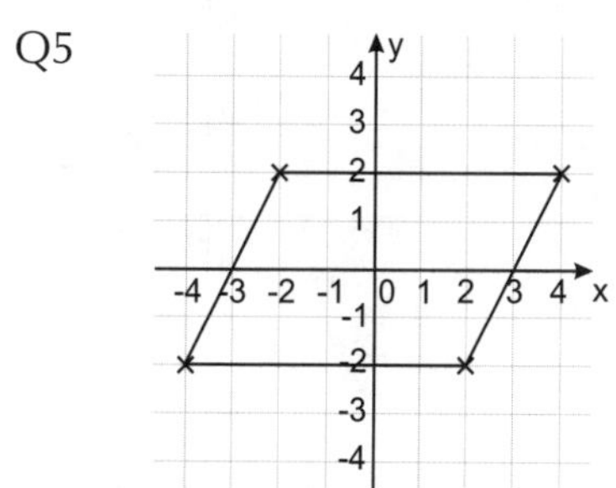

(2 marks for all points plotted and joined correctly, 1 mark for two or three points plotted correctly)
parallelogram or **quadrilateral**
(1 mark)

Q6 **(3, –2)** *(1 mark)*

Page 68 — Reflection

Q1

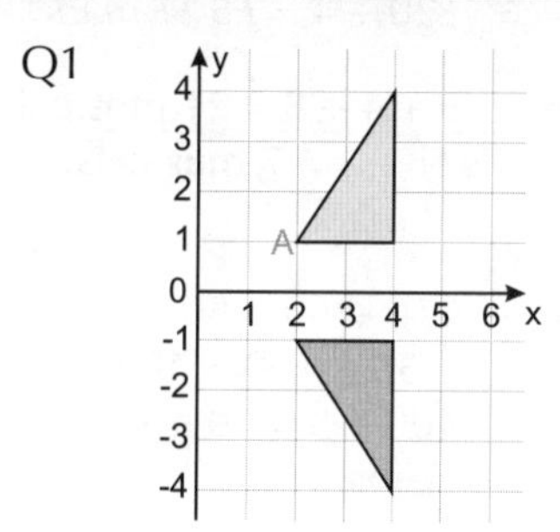

(1 mark)
(2, –1) *(1 mark)*

Q2

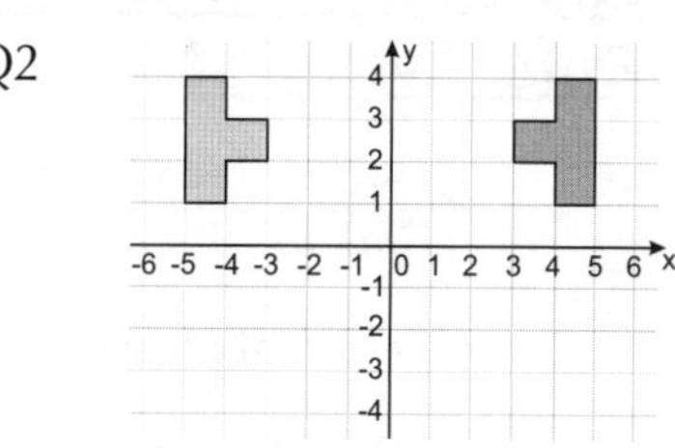

(1 mark)

Q3

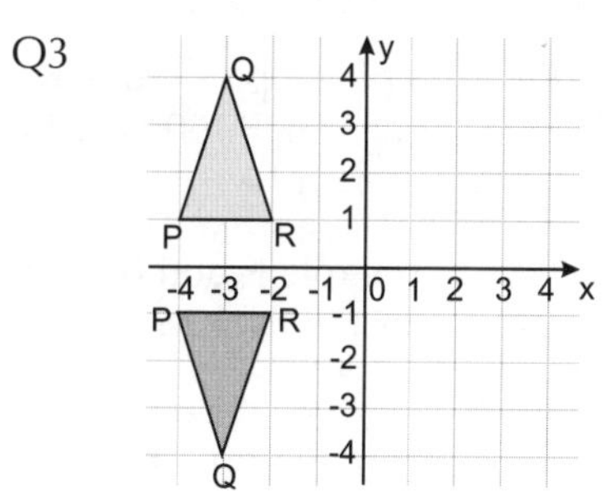

Q is at **(–3, –4)** in the reflected shape.
(1 mark for the correct coordinates)

Page 69 — Translation

Q1

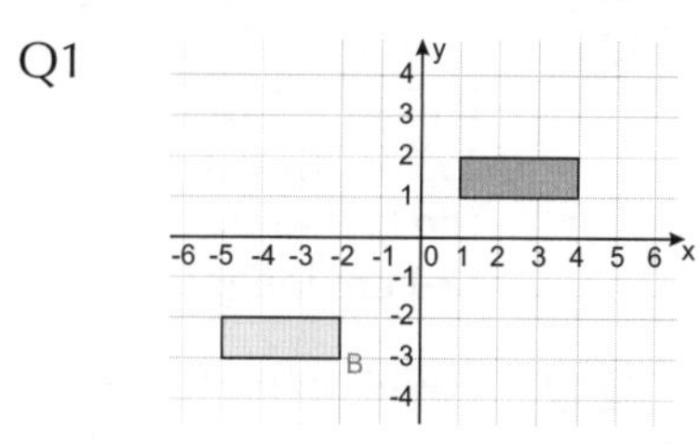

(1 mark)
(4, 1) *(1 mark)*

Q2 Move **5** units **right** and **5** units **down**. (1 mark)

Q3 **(–2, –3)** *(1 mark)*

Section Eight — Statistics

Pages 70-71 — Pie Charts

Q1 **Roller coaster** *(1 mark)*
Twister *(1 mark)*

Q2 $\frac{1}{2}$ of 20
= **10 tulips** *(1 mark)*
$\frac{1}{4}$ of 20
= **5 lilies** *(1 mark)*

Q3 360° ÷ **10** = **36°** *(1 mark)*
2 × 36° = **72°** *(1 mark)*

Q4

Animal	Number of people	Sector angle
Horse	2	60°
Cat	4	**120°**
Dog	6	**180°**

E.g.

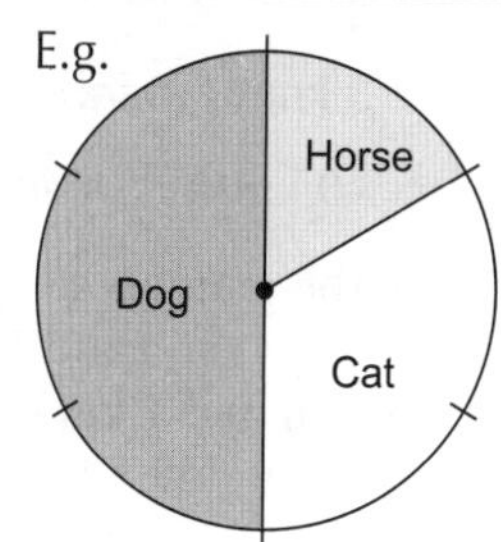

(2 marks — 1 mark for calculating all angles correctly, 1 mark for drawing pie chart accurately)

Q5 360° – 240° = **120°**
(1 mark)
$\frac{120}{360} = \frac{12}{36} = \frac{1}{3}$
$\frac{1}{3}$ of 30 = **10 people**
(1 mark)

Q6 Green:
$\frac{60}{360} = \frac{6}{36} = \frac{1}{6}$
$\frac{1}{6}$ of 60 = 10 clowns
Yellow:
$\frac{180}{360} = \frac{18}{36} = \frac{1}{2}$
$\frac{1}{2}$ of 60 = 30 clowns
10 + 30 = **40 clowns**
(1 mark)

Answers

Pages 72-73 — Line Graphs

Q1 **8 km** *(1 mark)*
50 miles = 10 × 5 miles
≈ 10 × **8 km** = **80 km**
(1 mark)

Q2

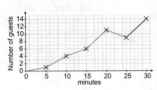

(1 mark)

11 – 4 = **7 guests**
(1 mark)

Q3

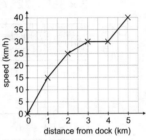

(1 mark)

3 km *(1 mark)*

40 km/h *(1 mark)*

The graph is steepest between 0 and 1 km, so **0 and 1 km** should be circled. *(1 mark)*

Pages 74-75 — The Mean

Q1 2 + 4 + 6 = **12**
12 ÷ 3 = **4** *(1 mark)*

Q2 3 + 5 + 10 = 18
18 ÷ 3 = **6** *(1 mark)*
2 + 3 + 4 + 7 = 16
16 ÷ 4 = **4** *(1 mark)*

Q3 The mean = 3 and there are 4 numbers, so the total sum of the numbers = 3 × 4 = 12.
12 – 1 – 4 – 5 = 2.
So the missing number = **2** *(1 mark)*

Q4 2 + 1 + 5 + 12 = 20
£20 ÷ 4 = **£5** *(1 mark)*

Q5 9 + 4 + 8 = 21 musicals
21 ÷ 3 = **7 musicals**
(1 mark)

Q6 110 + 60 + 80 + 50 + 100 = 400
400 ÷ 5 = **80 points**
(1 mark)

Pages 76-79 — Year Six Objectives Test

Q1 (3 + 8) × 4 = **11** × 4 = **44**
(1 mark)

Q2 **4 900 000** *(1 mark)*

Q3 1307 ÷ 1000 = **1.307**
(1 mark)

Q4 3 pineapples = 6 halves,
60p × 6 = 360p = **£3.60**
(1 mark)

Q5 The rule is add 6, so the next term is **26** *(1 mark)*

Q6 10% of 500 = 50,
20% of 500 = 50 × 2
= **100** *(1 mark)*

Q7 $\frac{1}{2} \times 10 \times 7 = \mathbf{35\ m^2}$
(1 mark)

Q8 $\frac{3}{4} \times \frac{2}{5} = \frac{6}{20} = \mathbf{\frac{3}{10}}$
(1 mark)

Q9 2.55 m = 255 cm,
1.15 m = 115 cm
255 – 115 = 140 cm
The ball of wool is now **140 cm** long. *(1 mark)*

Q10 Count on in steps of 1 from –8 to 1.
There are 9 steps, so the temperature has increased by **9 °C**.
(1 mark)

Q11 2 + 1 + 3 + 2 = 8 goals,
8 ÷ 4 = **2 goals** *(1 mark)*

Q12 Possible pairs: **5** and **1** or **4** and **2** *(1 mark)*

Q13

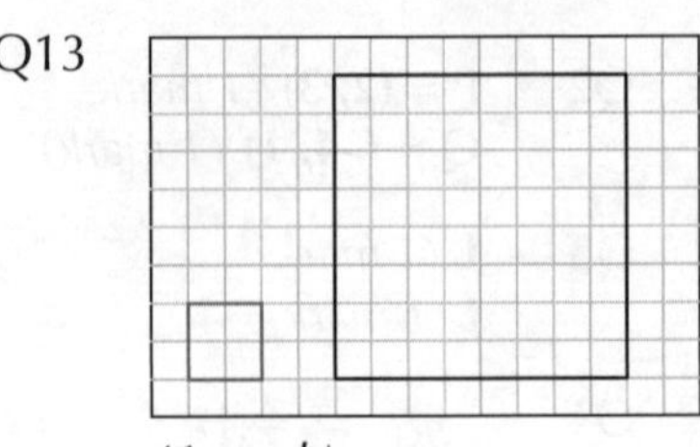

(1 mark)

Q14 **Triangular prism** *(1 mark)*

Q15 60 ÷ 5 = 12,
so s = **12** *(1 mark)*

Q16 360° – 130° – 50° – 75° = 105°, so a = **105°**
(1 mark)

Q17

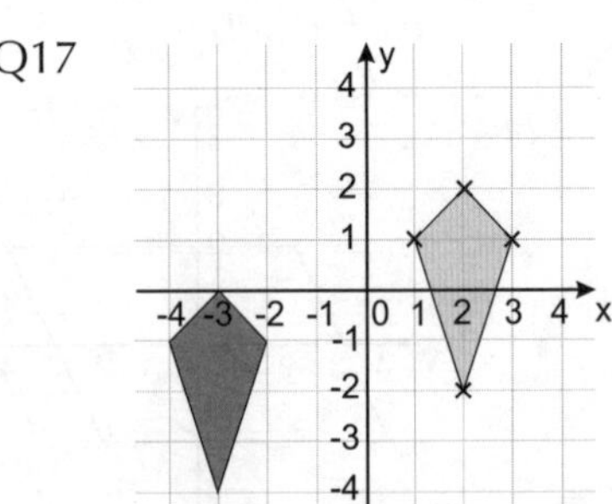

(2 marks — 1 mark for the correct point plotted, 1 mark for the correct translation)

Q18

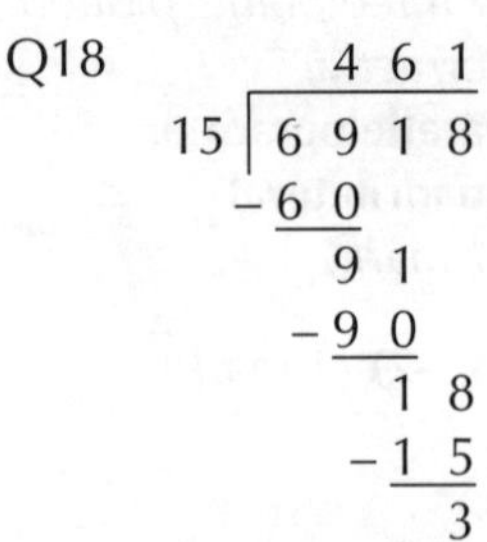

So each friend gets **£461** and there is a **remainder of £3 / £3 left over**
(1 mark for £461, 1 mark for remainder £3)